BRITISH BIRDS
in their
HABITATS

BRITISH BIRDS
in their
HABITATS

Ron Freethy

With line illustrations by Carole Pugh

THE CROWOOD PRESS

Frontispiece
Razorbill breeding on the Treshnish Islands, off
Mull.

First published in 1985 by
THE CROWOOD PRESS
Crowood House,
Ramsbury, Marlborough,
Wiltshire SN8 2HE.

British Library Cataloguing in Publication Data
Freethy, Ron
    British birds in their habitats.
    1. Birds—Great Britain—Habitat
    I. Title
    598.252′ 0941   QL690.G7

ISBN 0-946284-56-3

Design by Vic Giolitto

Set in 10 on 11 pt Bembo
by Quadraset Ltd, Midsomer Norton, Bath, Avon
Printed in Spain by Graficromo s.a., Cordoba

Contents

Acknowledgements

There are a number of people without whom this book would not have been produced in its present form. My wife Marlene typed the manuscript and, as always, made many constructive comments at that stage. My son Paul and Brian Lee both read the proofs and their eagle eyes came to my rescue on several occasions. Peter Leek of The Crowood Press and Michael Radford, who edited the book, did much to keep my writing to the point. As Editor of the British Naturalists' Association's journal *Country-Side*, I was able to draw on a reservoir of remarkably vivid and beautiful photographs. I am especially grateful to Will Bown, Michael Edwards, Robert Howe and Charles Linford for allowing me to include so many of their photographs and to Michael Chesworth, John Clegg, Reg Harrison, Eric Hosking, Brian Oldfield, Ray Palmer, Fritz Polking, Bill Wilkinson and the Royal Society for the Protection of Birds for permission to reproduce the photographs listed below. To Carole Pugh, who drew the splendid line illustrations, I am grateful both for her artistic ability and for her encouragement.

Ron Freethy

THORNEYHOLME HALL

Roughlee,
Lancashire.

Picture credits

Black & white photos

Will Bown: 30, 31, 64, 66 (bottom), 76, 81, 102, 140 (top left and right), 177, 192, 196.
Michael Chesworth: 13, 25.
John Clegg: 21, 200.
Michael Edwards: 15, 18, 22, 35, 38 (top), 40 (top and bottom), 50, 66 (top), 71, 75, 83 (top left and right, centre right, bottom right), 84, 103, 109, 111 (top and bottom), 112, 131, 135, 137 (bottom), 141 (top and bottom), 150, 154, 156, 166, 178, 181, 183 (bottom), 186, 187.
Ron Freethy: frontispiece, 34, 57, 80, 85 (top and bottom), 87, 89.
Reg Harrison: 139 (bottom).
Eric Hosking: 161, 183 (top).
Robert Howe: 174, 176, 185, 197, 198.
Charles Linford: 12, 14, 19, 26, 61 (bottom), 63 (top and bottom), 82, 83 (centre left and bottom left), 95, 99, 142, 146, 155, 167, 189.
Ray Palmer: 38 (bottom).
Fritz Pölking: 98.
Royal Society for the Protection of Birds: 170.
Bill Wilkinson: 61 (top).

Colour photos

Will Bown: Plates 11, 20, 25–26.
Michael Edwards: Plates 1, 8, 10, 13, 16–19.
Ron Freethy: Plates 2, 12, 15, 21, 23–24.
Robert Howe: Plates 4–7, 9, 14, 22.
Brian Oldfield: Plate 3.

Jacket photos

Front:
Long-eared owl – Michael Edwards
Oystercatcher – Michael Edwards
Waxwing – Robert Howe
Kestrel – Ron Freethy.

Back:
Kingfisher – Michael Edwards.

Introduction

The purpose of this book is to identify the various habitats occupied by birds by looking at the historical aspects, assessing the present situation and if possible indicating future prospects. There can be no doubt that until the last couple of centuries the only threat posed by *Homo sapiens* to the earth's genetic heritage came from hunting and gathering which very occasionally wiped out animal species, including a few birds, as well as some plants. We are now much more of a threat because the destruction we cause can be of a much more subtle nature. Thirteen thousand million dollars worth of pesticides found their way onto the world market during 1981 and this shows no signs of doing anything other than increasing. In France and Germany, for example, between 50% and 85% of bees are killed (the percentage depends upon the area studied) by these chemicals. 'So what?' says the insular bird watcher. We should not forget that bees pollinate plants and these provide food for birds and many insects which in turn are the staple diet of other birds. We disrupt these vital food chains at our peril.

A similar, and just as worrying a problem, concerns the acid rain which results from the build-up of inorganic acids from industrial discharges into the atmosphere. This can be produced in one country (in western Europe, for example) and carried to another (Scandinavia) where it defoliates the trees and once more the food webs so vital to the survival of birds and ourselves are disrupted. Recent work, however, suggests that another source of acidity may well be the decaying needles of conifers. Heavy metals, particularly lead, mercury and cadmium, are also accumulating to levels which are often worrying and sometimes positively alarming. Along roadsides, for example, the lead content of the soil, originating from petrol, can reach 300 grams per tonne whereas the natural level in the atmosphere is in the order of $0 \cdot 05$ grams per tonne.

In view of such statistics do we shrug our shoulders and concentrate on living it up before disaster strikes, or do we become neurotic pessimists? In my view we should do neither, but direct our efforts towards finding solutions. Birds are lively, active, colourful creatures which, compared with many other forms of life, are relatively easy to monitor. We should therefore count bird populations regularly – and a comparison of these counts will give an indication of the state of the environment. A study of birds in their habitats is not only enjoyable but may help us to survive, since we share the environment with them. This is the reason why some optimism will be apparent in each chapter, although the problems faced by certain species will not be avoided. There are many books covering the intricate details of each complex food web and it would serve no useful purpose to write another; for the reader who wishes for greater detail a full bibliography is provided. Instead, I have chosen to describe individual species within their habitats to enable the reader to identify them and understand the part each plays in the food webs.

When we hear of a bird threatened with extinction, we are often told intimate details of its anatomy and how complex the task of keeping the species alive is likely to be. In one sense the solution is much easier than this; in another it is much more difficult. How can this apparent paradox be resolved? The answer is not to bother about the bird itself, but to concentrate upon the environment in which it lives. If its habitat is preserved or even extended, then in almost every case the bird will be able to make good its losses. In some cases the demise may be due to alterations in climate, a process which has been going on since the birth of the earth and is the basis of evolution. I do not believe mankind should interfere with nature, but we should concentrate our attention and our financial resources on ensuring that we do not upset the delicate equilibrium.

1 Mixed Woodlands

But come the woodman with his axe
Into the sun-sweet glade
And what was once all beauty and grace
Is into firewood made
(Walter De La Mare, 'Logs')

Walter De La Mare's poem points to the fate of much of our woodlands and it is no surprise that some of our native tree-loving birds have struggled to thrive in the face of such pressure. This chapter will examine the development of our woodlands following the retreat of the ice, then go on to a brief consideration of the human activities which have so upset the natural balance. The main object, however, is to describe those birds which are still an integral part of our woodland scene. About 60% of breeding British land birds need trees and more than half of our butterflies and moths live in woodland, whilst some 15% of our flowers are woodland-based.

The ice

A series of glaciations affected much of Europe during the Pleistocene Period, the last – although there may be others to come – being known as the Worm. This came to an end about 10,000 years ago, but the ice-cap never came south of a line stretching between the Severn and the Thames, although it must have been pretty chilly even there.

As the ice melted, rising sea levels first separated Ireland from Britain and then the Dover–France land bridge was swamped. These events are still reflected in the relative distribution of European wildlife today. Ireland, for example, does not have any resident woodpeckers, whilst in Britain we have three, the green, the great spotted and the lesser spotted – plus that diminishing summer visitor the wryneck, which has not bred in Britain since 1981. This compares with the ten species found on the continent. Nor does Ireland have the pleasure of the company of the tawny owl. Europe has seventeen species of owl, compared with the six in Britain.

In Britain the development first of rough grassland followed by trees seems to have begun around 7000 BC. The first trees were probably dwarf willows, followed by birch and then by pine. By 5000 BC these pioneers had produced a habitat suitable for hardwood trees such as oak, elm, alder and ash. This occurred because the leaves of the earlier arrivals increased both the depth and the mineral content of the soil, thus providing the larger trees with both anchorage and the salts essential for healthy growth. Some minor trees requiring a fairly rich soil also made their appearance at this time, including hawthorn, blackthorn, rowan, holly and wild cherry. We know that this sequence is accurate because each species produces pollen grains which not only have their own unique shape but which are also almost indestructible. This, used in conjunction with accurate radio-carbon dating, has enabled botanists to construct a very accurate vegetational history. This initial period of dry and comparatively warm weather has been named the Boreal Period. As it neared its end trees such as lime, hornbeam, beech, whitebeam and poplar made their appearance.

About 5000 BC, a warm wet sequence known as the Atlantic Period began. It lasted until about 3000 BC, and it was during this time that sea levels rose considerably and further isolated Britain from Europe. During the next period, called the Sub-Boreal, which lasted from 3000 BC to 1 BC, the climate once more became warm and many of the peat bogs formed during the Atlantic Period dried out sufficiently to support active growth of woodland. From about the birth of Christ to AD 1000, the Sub-Atlantic Period, there was a return to damp mild weather ideal for the growth of deciduous trees but not at all to the liking of the Scots pine, which therefore suffered a dramatic decline. We are now in what is appropriately labelled the Recent Period and despite cold spells during the fourteenth and fifteenth centuries and again in the seventeenth and eighteenth most commentators are agreed that the overall trend is towards a warmer and perhaps drier climate, although it is only fair to report that a minority of pessimists are predicting the return of the ice, which would be even more disastrous to the vegetation than the hand of man ever could be.

Man's effect on the woodlands

Our ancestors were originally foragers and hunters with few permanent settlements and having little, if any, lasting impact on their environment. Forest clearance and settlement beginning about 5000 BC can be deduced from pollen analysis, which reveals increasing proportions of grasses and associated weeds, particularly the plantains, especially *Plantago lanceolata*. It is even possible to detect periods when settlements were abandoned, resulting in an increase in tree pollen. A succession of fairly limited forest clearances occurred in Bronze Age times and the last of these seems to have occurred in the English Lake District about 700 BC. From 50 BC onwards increased quantities of cereal pollen grains are found, obviously reflecting improved farming practices. Continuing demands for food and for timber for buildings and fuel for an expanding population which was becoming more and more industrial, not to mention commercially minded, resulted in the woodlands of Britain being reduced to a remnant. The reduction in vegetational cover was bound to affect the distribution and population of the animal life which totally depended upon it.

The woodland web of life

Green plants are able to make food by using the energy of sunlight to combine atmos-

pheric carbon dioxide with water. This process, termed photosynthesis, would only proceed very slowly without some chemical to speed it up and this accelerator is technically known as a catalyst. This is the function of the green pigment chlorophyll and thus green plants are the living organisms on which the food supply of all others depends. Thus plants are called primary producers. They are fed upon by vegetarian animals, referred to as primary consumers. They in turn are eaten by animals, known as secondary consumers. Finally each food chain will end with an arch-predator, the tertiary consumer. In a woodland an example of such a chain is:

SUN LIGHT	→	OAK TREE LEAVES	→	OAK EGGAR MOTH	→	BLUE TIT	→	TAWNY OWL
		CATERPILLAR						

sun light	→	primary producer	→	primary consumer	→	secondary consumer	→	tertiary consumer

Obviously things are not quite so simple as this since very few animals could survive by depending upon only one prey item and so the simple food chain becomes interwoven with others into a complex web. Each member of this community will have its own place in the scheme of things – its ecological niche. The story does not end here because when a living organism dies its body is quickly broken down by scavengers such as beetles and ants whilst the bacteria convert what is left to raw materials such as nitrates and other salts as well as releasing carbon dioxide which the green plant can then recirculate. Fungi also play a part in this breakdown process and the respiration of living organisms is another facet of this cycle. Oxygen is produced as a by-product during photosynthesis and this gas is used to release energy from food during respiration, which also releases carbon dioxide back into the atmosphere. An extract from Ted Hughes's poem 'Hawk Roosting' catches the meaning behind the woodland web, and is a lovely example of the marriage between art and accurate science.

'I sit in the top of the wood, my eyes closed
Inaction, no falsifying dream
Between my hooked head and hooked feet,
Or in sleep rehearse perfect kills and eat.

The sun is behind me
Nothing has changed since I began
My eye has permitted no change
I am going to keep things like this.'

Alas for many hawks, and the birds which share their habitat, things are no longer like this, but there are splendid areas in Britain – including the New Forest, Wales and the Lake District – where a typical woodland may still be studied in the peace of the early morning, broken only by the chatter of the language of birds.

The structure of a mature woodland

A typical wood may be divided into four main zones. These are the ground layer, made up of liverworts and mosses; the field layer, rich in flowers such as primrose, wood anemone, bluebell, ramson and dog's mercury, according to season; the shrub layer of small bushes and sapling trees; and finally the tree or canopy layer.

Some ornithologists divide these regions still further in an effort to produce for each woodland bird a personalised ecological niche. We must not, however, be too dogmatic for some species – the pied flycatcher, for example – can use all the zones at one time or another. It feeds in the canopy zone, and nests in the trunk or branches of the trees, but it may feed on insects found in the field and shrub layers and gather nesting material from the ground. In damp woodlands the bird is to be found perched on branches over water, periodically fluttering out to catch a fly before returning to its original perch. This is typical flycatcher behaviour and serves to identify the family. In Britain we have two breeding species, the pied and the more common spotted flycatcher.

Woodland birds

Pied flycatcher *Ficedula hypoleuca*
The pied flycatcher is a 13 centimetre long (about 5 inches) summer migrant and as many as 20,000 pairs may arrive during mid-May to breed, most departing during September. It shows a distinct preference for damp deciduous woodlands, mainly those skirting lakes or penetrated by streams. Its distribution these days seems to be on the western, damper, side of Britain, and breeding in the eastern counties is now a rare event. No doubt the removal of woodlands from these areas, plus the intensive agricultural practices involving the often ill-considered removal of hedgerows and over-liberal use of herbicides and insecticides which disrupt the food chains, have been the major factors accounting for the demise of the pied flycatcher in the east. It may well be that this loss of habitat in one area accounts for the breeding range of the species having gradually extended northwards. The male is easily recognised by his neat black-and-white plumage. The back is mainly black but there are contrasting patches of white on the forehead and along the wing bar, whilst the underparts are also white. The female is grey-brown above and she has no white on the forehead but she does have a prominent light-coloured wing bar. The preferred nest site is a natural hole in a deciduous tree, but there has been some adaptation to changing conditions and they will also use cavities in walls and buildings as well as nest boxes, which often allows them to make use of young, recently planted woodlands. The presence of pied flycatchers in a woodland can be of great advantage to the forester since they consume many insect pests, mainly on the wing, but they will also eat bark beetles and the larvae of moth caterpillars, which can defoliate trees, often with damaging results. This diet is similar to, but not identical with, that of the spotted flycatcher, whose British breeding population may be as high as 200,000 pairs.

Spotted flycatcher *Muscicapa striata*
The spotted flycatcher is much more widespread and, in contrast with the pied flycatcher, also occurs in Ireland. Slightly larger than the pied at 14 centimetres (5½ inches), both sexes are alike, being grey-brown above with darker spots and streaks of brown on the crown, whilst the breast is paler but still spotted and streaked with brown. The nest may be in a hole in a tree but more often the four or five eggs, which are greenish-white and speckled with red, are laid in a nest in a

junction between branch and trunk or in a
wall. One reason for its wide distribution is
its ready acceptance of a nest site in small
woodland, park or garden, as well as a liking
for nest boxes. I found whilst wardening a
small woodland reserve that I could allow
blue tits to raise a family in a nest box and
then remove the front to allow spotted
flycatchers to move into the larger space later
in the season.

Robin *Erithacus rubecula*

The robin is another species which makes use
of more than one of the woodland layers. It
sings, preens and roosts in the shrub layer,
especially if hazel, elder or hawthorn are
present, but feeds mainly in the field and
ground layers, being particularly fond of
bramble. This is also a favoured habitat of the
nightingale, but this elusive bird prefers the
thick shrub of common heathland, although

coppiced woodlands are also acceptable. In
Britain the robin is more or less resident,
but continental robins are highly mobile and
investigations carried out in Germany suggest
that they are able to detect magnetic north and
use this to orient themselves. This 'compass'
may well be a part of every brain cell, and
a similar mechanism has been hinted at in
studies of homing pigeons in America.

During autumn British robins become
aggressive and territorial and at this time both
sexes may hold individual territories. These
are obviously eroded during the spring when
the nest is built and the five or six pale-buff
eggs, spotted with red, are incubated by the
hen, who is fed by the male. The male helps to
feed the young, which can fly in a couple of
weeks or so, at which time they are some 14
centimetres (5½ inches) in length. Male and
female adults look alike, but the young lack
the red breast and the spots and streaks betray
their close affinity with the thrush family.

Robin – a common but often misunderstood
British resident.

Two or three broods may be produced in a good season and a new nest is almost always constructed for each. The population may be sharply depressed during a hard winter, but their ready acceptance of offerings on bird tables is an important survival factor. There is no doubt that the robin was originally a woodland bird, finding most of its insect food among the leaf litter, and this is still its niche over most of its European range.

Tree-creeper *Certhia familiaris*
In contrast with the flycatchers and the robin, the 12·5 centimetre (5 inch) tree-creeper is seldom found anywhere other than on the main trunk and branches of the larger species of tree. Its British distribution is almost identical with that of the spotted flycatcher. Feeding mainly on insects found on or in the bark, the tree-creeper begins its search close to the base of the tree and by means of jerky mouse-like movements works spirally up and around the trunk and upon reaching the top flies down to the base of the next tree to repeat the activity. The slender down-curved bill is ideal for extracting the insects and spiders whilst the streaky brown back provides perfect camouflage against the barky background. Beneath there are areas of white, and the eye stripe and wing bars are prominent.

Tree-creepers and the woodpeckers have reacted to a similar problem in a similar way. Climbing trees successfully requires some means of support and both families have solved this problem by evolving long stiff central tail feathers which work like a prop, enabling the bird to lean backwards away

Tree-creeper collecting food.

from the tree and survey the scene at their leisure. No problem arises at the time of the moult: only one tail feather is lost at a time. The British population of tree-creepers is estimated at between 150,000 and 200,000 pairs and there is reason to believe that it has extended its range in recent years and now nests even in the Outer Hebrides. It is still very dependent upon trees both for feeding and for breeding. The twiggy nest is often hidden behind loose bark and both cock and hen labour industriously to build the nest, but the hen does most of the work during the two weeks it takes to incubate the six eggs. The male takes his full share of the feeding before the young can fly and the second clutch of eggs which invariably follows is laid.

No bird gets a better view of the woodland structure than the tree-creeper as it works its way up the trunk of the tallest tree, beginning at ground level, looking down in turn on the field layer and shrub layer, and finally perching in the canopy.

This layering is seen at its best in a British woodland dominated by oak and it is to this habitat that we must pay most attention if we are to understand the biology of our woodland birds, but we also have woods dominated by other broad-leaved trees, including birch and beech.

Birds of the oak woods

Pheasant *Phasianus colchicus*
No bird on the British list can have been responsible for more ecological disruption than the introduced pheasant, even though it

The pheasant – one of the most colourful birds introduced into Britain.

Pheasants are still popular game birds in Britain.

is not the bird which has been responsible but rather those who shoot it. The strongest available evidence tends to support deliberate introduction by the Romans of one or perhaps two sub-species of pheasant – one originating in the Caucasus and the other, the ring-necked type, coming from China. In the medieval forest pheasants were only incidental game but by the eighteenth century they had become more popular and from the nineteenth century onwards pheasant rearing and shooting had become almost a major industry, a position maintained to some extent today. On the credit side large numbers of new woods were planted, and threatened ones saved, to provide cover for pheasants, but the debit side is somewhat heavier because gamekeepers naturally enough responded to their masters' demands by a ruthless extermination of any suspected predator. Guns, poison baits, gin traps and nest raiding all ensured a ready supply of hook-billed strong-taloned birds, as well as hundreds of mammals, swinging in the wind on the gamekeepers' gibbets which were so

much a part of the Victorian country scene. With the passing of Bird Protection Acts such extreme pressure has been reduced, but we must not imagine that some illegal methods are not practised in an effort to maintain the vulnerable game bird at artificially high population levels.

The male pheasant is a most handsome fellow, varying considerably in size from 55 to 90 centimetres (22–36 inches) with a copper-brown body, dark-green head with red wattles, and a long tail. Despite this striking appearance he is more often heard than seen as his penetrating 'koo-kok' call echoes clearly through the woodland. His smaller mate – usually under 60 centimetres (24 inches) – is browner and utters a quiet whistle; her tail is also shorter and she makes the maximum use of available cover. Her retiring attitude and plumage make her very difficult to see as she sits for about 25 days on a clutch varying from eight to fifteen eggs. It was such a hen pheasant which provided me with my first memorable bird-watching experience at the age of eight. After listening

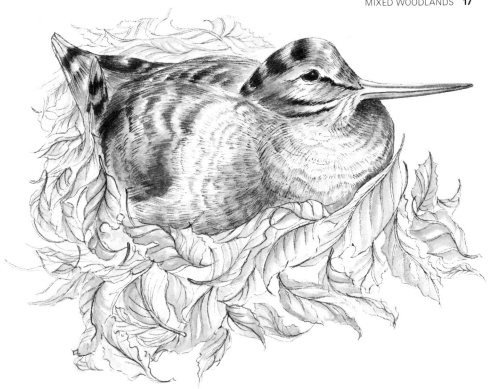

Woodcock.

to the dawn chorus in a Lakeland wood, my father and I looked for a dry patch of bracken on which to sit and take breakfast. As my father sat, a hen pheasant 'exploded' from beneath him and left us both convulsed with laughter after a moment of nerve-jangling panic. Fortunately, my father's backside missed the fifteen light-brown shiny eggs, and like good conservationists we left the area and were pleased to note the return of the female pheasant within half an hour of her narrow escape.

This preference for breeding and feeding in the field and ground layers of a wood is shared with the woodcock, although the two birds do not compete for food. Pheasants take mainly vegetable matter, such as seeds, roots, leaves and fruits. Any insect food taken by the adults is purely incidental, being attached to the chosen vegetation. Young pheasants may take more animal food than their parents but the woodcock's bill shape rules out any real competition, and each species has its own niche.

Woodcock *Scolopax rusticola*

The woodcock has a long probing bill ideally shaped for pushing deeply into soft ground in search of worms, insect larvae and other invertebrates. Like the pheasant, this wading bird is also highly prized by sportsmen, who enjoy trying to hit a woodland bird which roosts by day, but when flushed twists and turns along the woodland rides and between the trees, providing a very tricky target. It is very good to eat and a thorough knowledge of its habits during the Middle Ages enabled bird catchers to keep up with the demands from the kitchens. At dusk the birds (probably both sexes) tend to fly along recognised routes to preferred feeding areas, and during the breeding season patrol around their woodland territories with a slow and measured wing-beat uttering an unforgettable call consisting of three grunts followed by a higher pitched 'tis-ic'. This is called 'roding' and it follows a definite and predictable route. Special nets called cockshuts were stretched between trees and across rides, and the fact that this practice was once widespread can be seen by reference

The woodpigeon incubating its two eggs on a fragile nest of twigs.

to place-names such as Cockshoot, Cockleys, Cockroad and Cock-lea. Doubtless the wood-cock was more common when our woodlands were more extensive but our breeding population of about 50,000 pairs is greatly swelled by a winter influx of continental birds which find Britain's oceanic climate mild enough to provide sufficient feeding stations in all but the most severe of winters. The position of the large eyes at the sides of the head means that the feeding bird is able to see to the sides and even behind it, giving the woodcock advance warning of the approach of predators.

Woodpigeon *Columba palumbus*

In contrast with the woodcock, which has been reduced by loss of habitat, the wood-pigeon has proved to be a much more adapt-able species which during the last two or three hundred years has abandoned its traditional habitat of deciduous woodland and learned to take advantage of arable farmland with its associated hedges and shelter belts. It has also proved able to thrive in city parks and the resident population of between 3 and 5 million pairs is increased by enormous numbers of winter migrants which pour in from the continent, and whilst they still roost in trees they spend the day often making devastating feeding sorties on to farmland, where they are rightly regarded as pests. They also wander about at random and have thus tended to avoid coming into contact with lethal doses of insecticides.

At 40 centimetres (16 inches) this species is our largest pigeon and is recognised by a conspicuous white patch on its neck which accounts for its alternative name of ring dove, the words dove and pigeon being synonymous. In flight the white wing bar also shows up clearly and helps to distinguish *Columba palumbus* from the less common stock dove, which is known scientifically as *Columba oenas* and which is also resident in woodlands, but is the smaller bird at some 32 centimetres (about 13 inches). Instead of the

Hen sparrow-hawk at her nest.

neck ring, the stock dove has an iridescent green on the side of the neck and black tips to the flight feathers and tail. It shows a distinct preference for well established deciduous woodlands, especially those having some trees past maturity and thus liberally supplied with nesting holes. Despite substantial loss of habitat between the seventeenth and nineteenth centuries as the industrial revolution gathered momentum, the stock dove managed to expand its range if not its population and it bred in Scotland for the first time in 1877. Some increase in population was noted from 1900 to 1950 but from that time there was the tendency towards the indiscriminate use of pesticides and the less mobile stock dove suffered more than the woodpigeon. Despite substantial losses, however, the breeding population of the stock dove is still in the order of 100,000 pairs. Birds such as the stock dove are in the position of primary consumers and if they are vulnerable to pollution from poisons such as dieldrin and aldrin then how

much more theatening these must be to birds such as the sparrow-hawk and the tawny owl, which are at the top end of the food chain.

Sparrow-hawk *Accipiter nisus*
The sparrow-hawk is at the moment emerging from a period of great crisis, culminating during the 1960s when the additional burden imposed by chemicals on top of loss of habitat and persecution by gamekeepers to preserve pheasant stocks had almost reduced this lovely bird to extinction. In 1962 it was given special protection and this certainly helped the cause of the sparrow-hawk. Like most of the hawks the female is much larger than her mate, being at 38 centimetres (15 inches) about 10 centimetres (4 inches) bigger than the male. Some ornithologists have expressed the opinion that this size discrepancy has evolved to allow the female to protect the young against the cannibalistic tendencies of the cock. This I cannot accept and I favour the alternative theory which suggests that having sexes of different sizes means that they will take

different prey and therefore avoid coming in direct competition with each other. This could be very important at times when food is at a premium, as in hard winters. Both have short round wings and a long tail, a combination allowing for quick twisting and balanced flight between trees. The female is brown on the back, which contrasts sharply with the lighter belly, and the breast is attractively barred with brown. The male is dark grey above and the barring on the chest is a rusty red. Sparrow-hawks often breed in conifer woods as well as deciduous areas and also in parklands, but they do much of their hunting across fields and along hedges, and thus they were bound to pick up pesticides from the small birds such as dunnocks, finches, thrushes and skylarks which make up the bulk of their diet. The effects of these poisons have been carefully studied and two main points have been noted. First, the poisons seem to accumulate in the body fat of the bird and as these reserves are not drawn upon until the individual is under pressure the deadly substances may remain, in ambush, for many years. During a severe winter the already weakened bird draws on these fat deposits and the poisons are then released into the bloodstream at the very time when the bird is least able to cope. Second, and perhaps even more subtly, the poisons interfere with the reproductive cycle, and in severe cases may prevent breeding altogether. Even when the four or five eggs are produced they have been found to have such thin shells that they are crushed beneath the weight of the hen bird, which undertakes the five-week incubation period on her own, relying on her mate to provide her with food – a task he undertakes for both the hen and the young. He brings mostly small birds, but Brian Oldfield once watched a cock sparrow-hawk kill and skin a weasel before presenting it to the hen, who took it back to her brood in the nest. At the present time there are about 20,000 pairs of sparrow-hawks breeding in Britain and the losses still apparent in the deciduous woodlands of the south-east are being more than balanced by gains due to the birds using the maturing and largely undisturbed forestry plantations in Wales, northern England and

Scotland. The rides and clearings in such plantations are useful to sparrow-hawks, who usually have a favourite spot where the prey is taken and plucked at leisure. This area is littered with feathers, bits of flesh and other debris. An investigation of this debris will give a fair indication of the prey being taken and will show that the main diet is birds. This can be confirmed by an analysis of the disgorged pellets and it can be established that the diurnal bird-eating sparrow-hawk does not seriously compete with the nocturnal mammal-eating tawny owl, which also frequents deciduous woodland. Care must be taken, however, not to take too much notice of direct comparison of pellet contents since sparrow-hawks dismember their prey and owls swallow it whole, and in some cases alive. The digestive juices of the sparrow-hawk are much stronger than those of owls and the pellets of the latter will always reveal more bones due to this lack of digestive efficiency. Like the sparrow-hawk, owls also have favourite areas where they can rest and digest their meal in peace.

Tawny owl *Strix aluco*
The tawny owl is a species which was also affected to some degree by poisons, but much less than the diurnal sparrow-hawk. This is because the owl feeds on small mammals such as bank voles, wood mice and shrews which all tend to be resident in the woodland and seldom venture out into the surrounding agricultural areas. If it does take birds they are usually such species as blue and great tits which tend to remain within a short distance of their birthplace unless the weather is really cold, a period when few agricultural pesticides are being used. In my own analysis of tawny owl pellets I have found mammals to make up over 80% of the majority of the castings. Occasionally birds assume a major importance, but there are one or two really confusing records when the pellets have little in them but grass. A probable explanation has been put forward by Brian Oldfield as a result of a session photographing tawny owls feeding their young. He noted that on calm, clear nights the parents fed their young very infrequently on very nutritious and com-

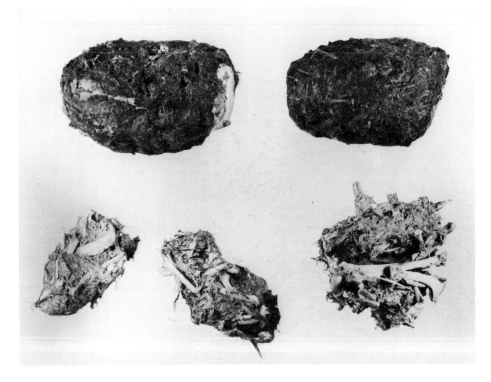

Owl pellets – barn owl (top), long-eared owl (bottom).

paratively bulky mammals. During wet and windy nights the mammals tended to stay under cover and in any case would be difficult to see. Earthworms, however, are easily washed out of their burrows, and the owl picks these up and feeds them to the young. This diet is, however, much less nutritious and the photographer is delighted to find that the owl may pay twenty or thirty visits on each night when wind and rain pound down on his hide. There is also a lot of liquid in a worm which would make pellet formation difficult, and to add the essential bulk the parents bring grass to the owlets and push it down their often reluctant throats. This explains the grassy pellets and since Oldfield's work I have analysed pellets and graded my results according to the weather. Of 100 randomly selected pellets collected after calm cold February nights only 5 had substantial quantities of grass. Out of 100 randomly selected pellets collected following wet and windy February nights 89 contained grass and also *setae* (bristles) from earthworms.

The tawny owl is widely distributed and quite common (70,000 to 100,000 pairs breed) throughout mainland Britain but is absent from the Isle of Man, from the outer isles of Scotland and from Ireland. It is easily recognised, being 38 centimetres (15 inches) long with a large round head into which are sunk large dark eyes without the orange orbital rings found in the long-eared owl of the coniferous woods and the short-eared owl which frequents open moorland. The plumage is rufous-brown above, although some birds are much greyer, but both types have streaks of dark brown or black but with white on the shoulders and wing coverts. The underparts are buff-coloured but heavily streaked with brown. The breeding call is the familiar 'tu-whit, tu-whoo' (the male calls 'tu-whit', the female replies 'tu-whoo'), but territorial disputes and feeding calls involve the use of high-pitched and persistent 'kee-wik, kee-wik' calls.

Tree holes are favoured nest sites and so

deciduous woodland of mixed age is an ideal habitat, the owl laying from two to four eggs on the floor of the hole without the benefit of nesting material. These are incubated for about a month by the female who fiercely defends her young. They can fly within five weeks of hatching. During this time both adult birds are busy hunting and it is at this time that their huge eyes really come into their own. Owls cannot see in total darkness, but their eyes are adapted to make use of very dim light and in any case total darkness is rare in the natural world. Some appreciation of the owl's eye may be gained by an inspection of the structure of the retina. Two types of cell are found which are called rods and cones due to their respective shapes: the cones are sensitive to colour whilst the rods register only the intensity of light. In the owl's eye there are few cones but large batteries of rods which enable the bird to see at very low light levels. In addition to what amounts to an image intensifier, owls also possess acute hearing and although they can catch food on the wing (the feathers are soft and serve to muffle the sound during flight) the method preferred is to remain still on a perch and then drop onto the prey. This is then killed by the powerful grip of the talons or even a sharp nip with the bill.

Recent work on owls suggests that vision in low-intensity light may not be as good as previously thought and that hearing may be equally and perhaps even more important. In many species of owl, including the tawny, one ear is higher than the other and this may be useful in judging distance. The facial disc, a prominent feature of most owls, is now thought to focus sound waves and funnel them towards the ears. It is thus quite clear that more work needs to be done to unravel the intricate details of owl senses and diet. Whether the owl takes mainly earthworms and mammals or not, the smaller woodland birds certainly recognise it as a predator and this accounts for the massed attacks on it called 'mobbing'. Any owl discovered roost-

ing in a tree during the daylight hours is subjected to an unmerciful battering by a surprisingly well co-ordinated bunch of small birds of several species. Eventually the tormented owl can take this treatment no longer and glides away through the woodland in search of a quieter roost. The slow measured wing-beat of *Strix aluco* makes it easy to identify. Another family of birds with an equally characteristic flight pattern is the woodpeckers, which have a low looping flight taking them from branch to branch across a woodland clearing.

Green woodpecker *Picus viridis*

Both sexes are a delicate green above with a yellowish rump and grey-green underparts. There is a red area on the crown on both sexes, but this is more extensive in the male. A close look at the moustachial stripe is, however, a certain guide to sex. In the hen bird this and an area around the eye are uniformly black whilst in the male these markings have a red centre. The green at 32 centimetres (12–13 inches) is by far the largest of the British woodpeckers. The great spotted is about 24 centimetres (9½ inches), the lesser spotted 15 centimetres (6 inches), and the wryneck just a little larger at 16·5 centimetres (6½ inches).

During the last hundred and fifty years the green woodpecker has been gradually extending its range northwards and since 1950 this expansion has been even more marked and the bird has now penetrated deep into Scotland. I can remember as a boy in the 1940s and early 1950s scouring the Cumbrian woodlands in search of the elusive new addition to the county's breeding birds. In these same woods the loud laughing call of the yaffle, as it is often called, is now a regular sound. Some have even managed to penetrate into areas dominated, or almost so, by conifers – this being almost certainly due to the green woodpecker's association with the wood ant. The powerful claws enable the bird to scratch into the huge mounds of vegetation of which the ants construct their nests and the juicy larvae are exposed. The green woodpecker makes further use of the social insect in a fascinating piece of behaviour

Opposite
Tawny owls are present in most small woods and parks in Britain.

Woodpeckers: Lesser spotted (**top**)
Great spotted (**middle**)
Green (**bottom**).

known as anting. Most ornithologists agree that the bird dancing up and down on the ants' nest quivering its wings and obviously enjoying itself brings into play the insect's defence mechanism, in which a spray of formic acid is produced. Ants do not sting but bite and then squirt the acid into the cut. Several theories have been put forward, but the most acceptable to me is that the formic acid kills off the feather lice. This can easily be demonstrated by extracting formic acid from the ants and then dropping feather lice into the liquid. Almost all the lice are quickly destroyed. Other species also find anting an ideal method of delousing themselves. The jay is another bird well practised in the art.

In addition to its powerful bill *Picus viridis* has a long coiled tongue which is barbed and rough at the tip and this is ideal for seeking out insects deep in the wood of trees, and also ants in their nests. The fact that the nostrils are near the base of the bill enables the bird to breathe at the same time as extracting food. The salivary glands are also greatly enlarged and produce copious amounts of sticky fluid, enabling the tongue to function as an insect trap. Because of its ability to live almost entirely on a diet of ants the green woodpecker is found in the field and ground layers of the woodland much more often than the other members of the family.

Great spotted or Pied woodpecker
Dendrocopos major
This woodpecker is easily recognised by its black-and-white appearance with red undertail coverts. The male can be distinguished by a red spot on the nape. Great spotted woodpeckers have the looping flight typical of woodpeckers but they move across the woodland paths and rides much more quickly than the green. Both sexes drum on hollow branches, the sound carrying quite a distance, and this mechanically produced breeding call separates the woodpeckers from the songbirds, which are one rung ahead on the evolutionary ladder. A further point of distinction is found in the method of feeding the young: nestling songbirds gape to persuade their parents to push food into their mouths whereas in woodpeckers it is the

adults which open their mouths and the young which press into their bills to take food.

During the nineteenth century the great spotted woodpecker almost became extinct in Britain. Several factors have been suggested to account for this, including predation by red squirrels and extensive felling of woodland. Whatever the reasons may have been there has been a rapid recovery this century and it now breeds throughout mainland Britain wherever there are suitable trees. Like all woodpeckers, however, it is absent from the Isle of Man and Ireland and the presence of a single bird drumming in Northern Ireland during 1972 can hardly be regarded as proof of breeding. The nest hole is some 7 centimetres (2½ inches) in diameter and extends to a depth of 30 centimetres (12 inches), but before the final selection of site several trial borings are made. Each tunnel is usually directed upwards for

Old elm stump with woodpecker's nest hole.

The jay was once ruthlessly hunted for its colourful feathers.

the first few centimetres, obviously in an effort to keep out rain, and my observations in woods of Cumbria and southern Scotland suggest that the hole is drilled on the opposite side from the prevailing wind and seldom faces direct sunlight. In northerly parts birch and Scots pine are frequently selected but elsewhere oak is preferred, with sycamore and alder also being popular. The populations of British woodpeckers are often substantially increased by the influx of winter visitors from northern Europe.

Lesser spotted or Barred woodpecker *Dendrocopos minor*

This woodpecker has a more southerly distribution than its larger cousin, and its more retiring nature makes it a difficult bird to census. It can be distinguished from the great spotted by the lack of white shoulder patches and the prominent white barring across the dark back. There is no sign of red

under the tail coverts. The male lesser spotted woodpecker has a red crown whereas this is dull white in the female. In addition to drumming, usually on a side branch as opposed to the main trunk favoured by the greater spotted, both sexes also produce a shrill 'ki-ki-ki' call note which reminds me very much of the sound made by courting kestrels. All the woodpeckers have two important adaptations to woodland life: two of the four toes point forwards and two backwards (termed zygodactylous), giving a firm pincer-like grip on almost any surface, and the two central tail feathers like those of the tree-creeper are specially strengthened so that when the bird leans backwards they can be used as props. The food of the lesser spotted woodpecker consists in the main of arboreal insects such as moth and bark beetle larvae, but occasionally plant material is eaten and I have seen birds take elder and hawthorn fruit. They do not seem able, however, to overcome their shyness and even in the hardest of winters they rarely visit bird tables and other feeding sites. There seems no doubt that the presence of all species of woodpecker is an advantage to the forester in keeping down potentially expensive pests.

Jay *Garrulus glandarius*

Although the crow family in general is not these days an important part of the woodland avifauna there seems little doubt that the jay, with its love of acorns and a tendency to bury food for future use, has been a significant factor in the spread of oak woods.

The jay has not, despite its advantage to the forester, managed to live down the generally evil reputation of the crow family. It has been persecuted for many years because of its occasional tendency to eat pheasant eggs and chicks to supplement its natural diet of fruits and the young of small mammals. The body colour is a warm pinkish brown, but it is darker on the back and when it flies the white rump contrasts sharply with the black tail, and the white-and-blue wing pattern is most attractive. It was these exquisitely patterned and at times almost translucent blue feathers which almost led to the extinction of the jay due to the greed of the millinery trade which always had a ready sale for such treasures. Following the formation of an active and at times semiviolent 'Anti-Feather League' (later to become the RSPB), this pressure was removed, and although some jays are still shot the campaign against vermin is much reduced and it is pleasing to know that the raucous chattering from which the jay gets its scientific name *Garrulus* is now becoming more and more common in our woodlands. Thick cover is preferred as a nest site and the female lays five or six eggs which she incubates mainly herself in just over a fortnight, although the male does help to feed the young, which can usually fly about three weeks after hatching. It is during this period that jays can be a bit of a menace as they eat young birds, especially those of the titmouse family.

Woodland titmice (the family *Paridae*)

In Britain the great tit and blue tit frequent deciduous woodlands, whilst in conifer woods (see Chapter 2) we have coal and crested tits and marsh and willow tits are found in damper habitats. The long-tailed tit, which is not related to the *Parus* tits, also occurs in deciduous woodland. Thus the naturalist wandering through a typical lowland woodland will regularly come in contact with three species of tit, the great, the blue and the long-tailed.

Great tit *Parus major*

The great tit had its origins in Britain's ancient woodlands, as did the blue tit, but both quickly dovetailed their life histories into the pattern of human activities and can now exist almost anywhere providing there is some semblance of tree cover and sufficient food. At 14 centimetres (5½ inches), *Parus major* is the largest of the family. It has a black head against which the white cheeks stand out clearly and there is a prominent black line running down the yellow breast and belly. In some males the lower extremity of the black line divides into two, one line running down each thigh. This species has increased rapidly in recent years due to several factors, including increased tree planting (including conifers) and a sequence of mild winters, despite 1962–3, 1979 and 1981–2. There is also an increasing number of houses with gardens owned by people who enjoy feeding birds. Left to its own devices, the great tit feeds on spiders, worms, seeds and fruit buds, which are often reached by quite astounding feats of acrobatics. On one occasion I observed a great tit not only walking up the trunk of a tree, but actually turning round and descending the tree head first in its search for food in the cracks of the bark, a behaviour pattern normally associated with the nuthatch. If sufficient natural food is available, the tits breeding in our woodlands probably winter there, but during autumn and winter the population of this species and that of the blue tit is swelled by an influx of European visitors.

Blue tit *Parus caeruleus*

The blue tit is only 11·5 centimetres (4½ inches) long. The dominant colours are blue and yellow and although it has white cheeks

Great tit (**top**) and blue tit (**bottom**).

the blue head and lack of black line down the chest and belly easily distinguish it from *Parus major*.

Long-tailed tit *Aegithalos caudatus*
The long-tailed tit differs from both having a very tiny body, basically pink, black and white in colour, and its recorded size of 14 centimetres (5½ inches) includes the comparatively long tail. It also differs from the *Parus* family by not using a hole or nest box for breeding, preferring to construct a beautifully fashioned domed nest. As a breeding bird it is widely distributed and in the colder months of the year it tends to sweep through the upper branches of trees searching for the larvae of insects hibernating there but also doing some damage to buds. The 'see-see-

see' call usually indicates their presence long before the flock is sighted among the high branches swaying in the wind. They are often associated with other species, making up what is known as a 'gypsy flock', which usually includes the *Parus* tits, tree-creepers and the agile nuthatch, which has expanded its range in recent years.

Nuthatch *Sitta europaea*

The nuthatch is a dumpy little bird of some 14 centimetres (5½ inches). Its upper parts are bluish-grey and the lower parts fawn, but the chin is much paler. The flanks are of a rich chestnut-red whilst passing through the eye is a prominent streak which begins at the neck and ends at the base of the bill. The short tail is also bluish-grey but is marked with black and white. Although the sexes are quite similar in appearance the female is considerably duller than her mate. The nuthatch is a resident bird, strictly aboreal in habits, but unlike the tree-creeper and woodpeckers it does not receive any extra support from its tail, which is soft and short and lacks strengthened feathers. What the bird does have is very powerful claws which grip the trunk so tightly that it can walk freely not only up and around the trunk but also straight down it without any problems at all.

Although insects and their larvae are eaten, the nuthatch (its old name is the nut-hatchet), as its name implies, is a nut eater which is strongly attracted to oak woods, especially those with an under-storey of hazel. The method of opening a nut is to wedge it into a crevice and hammer it with the powerful bill until the nut is finally cracked and the juicy kernel exposed. The high piping 'pee-pee-chew' sound is easily recognised in the spring woodlands. The clutch of from six to eleven eggs is laid in a nest sited in a large tree hole which is plastered up by the bird until the diameter is small enough for its liking. Nut-hatches are beginning to take kindly to nest boxes and bird tables and these adaptations have allowed them to extend their range of habitats – something which is already a

Nuthatch (left)
Tree-creeper – note tail feathers used as a prop (right).

feature of the life of the blackbird and the thrushes, which were originally woodland dwellers (see Chapter 8).

Most of the birds resident in our woodlands begin their breeding cycle early in spring and given a pleasant sunlit day in late February or early March the trees may ring with the 'tee-cher, tee-cher, tee-cher' song of the great tit, the bell-like notes of the nuthatch, the cooing of the woodpigeon, the 'coughing' of the cock pheasant, and the clattering chatter of the jay. Robins, wrens and blackbirds add their notes to the woodland symphony and should the walker enter their territory the robin 'tic-tic-tics' its alarm call, keeping time as precisely as a metronome, and the wren follows a similar pattern but at an increased tempo. The drumming of the woodpecker, the hooting of the owl and the thin variable notes of the blue tit all play their role in the

part-song of the woodland choir. During April and May this choir is strengthened by the summer visitors, including the redstart and those lovely little birds the warblers. These are of two groups, the leaf warblers, genus *Phylloscopus*, and those of the typical genus *Sylvia*.

Warblers

Wood warbler *Phylloscopus sibilatrix*

The wood warbler is the only British bird which may be said to be confined to closed canopy woodland for breeding and feeding. It chases insects on leaves and may even leap into the air to catch a particularly succulent item before returning to its perch, where it stands in typical posture with wings drooped. Despite its feeding niche high in the trees it prefers to nest on the ground amongst a tangle of undergrowth. Warblers are hard to distinguish by physical appearance but a close look at the 12·5 centimetre (5 inch) wood warbler will show a greenish back, and a

Chiffchaff – one of the earliest migrants to arrive in spring.

yellow breast contrasting neatly with a white belly. Its most distinguishing feature is a yellow eye stripe. The song is, like those of all warblers, quite distinctive and consists of two phrases, a high quivering trill and a repetitive 'puu-puu-puu-puu', which are combined together in a most melodic manner.

Willow warbler *(Phylloscopus trochilus)* and Chiffchaff *(Phylloscopus collybita)*

Two other warblers are the easily confused willow warbler and the chiffchaff; the former prefers open areas of woodland whilst the latter is a bird of the woodland edge, and both species must therefore have benefited from the thinning out of dense woodland and the creation of coppice clearings. Both are 11 centimetres (4½ inches) long and are very similar in appearance, the legs of the willow warbler being described as pinkish whilst those of the chiffchaff are dark. The body of the chiffchaff is also darker. There is, however, a great deal of individual variation and by far the best way to distinguish the two

in summer is by their song. The chiffchaff repeats its own name whilst the willow warbler produces a much more imaginative and descending cadence ending in an accomplished flourish. Neither of these species can, in my view, compare with the larger blackcap, which perches high in the canopy and pours out a rich clear warbling song.

Blackcap *Sylvia atricapilla*

The nest of the blackcap is usually sited in shrub or even in the field layer, the structure being so delicately woven out of grass and roots that one can often see straight through it. I was at a loss to explain the evolutionary logic of such a structure until a wet day in July 1977. Rain sluiced down from a leaden sky and hissed onto the leaves which, weighted with water, served as funnels directing rain into nests. In the course of a depressing hour I looked at the nests of several species which I

The blackcap – a summering warbler becoming increasingly common in winter.

had previously mapped on a bird census form, only to find most of them full of water and drowned nestlings. Fearing the worst I approached the nest of the blackcap sited in a briar patch. Water was dripping into the nest from the overhanging leaves but merely passed straight through the strands of grass, leaving the young no more than damp and very active indeed. The parent birds both continued to feed them, no doubt finding plenty of insect prey literally floating about. Male and female blackcaps can easily be distinguished by the male's black cap and the brown cap of his mate. This feature also makes the species easy to distinguish from other warblers. Whilst the food is predominantly insects, blackcaps do take fruits in the autumn and winter as well as showing an increasing tendency to visit bird tables for scraps. This may well partly account for an increasing number of recent records of overwintering. This is yet another example of the ability of birds to adapt to an ever-changing environment.

Birds of birch woods

Whilst our oak woods are by far the richest, other types of woodland – particularly of birch and beech – are the permanent or temporary homes of specialist feeders. Natural birch woods are still found in northern and upland areas of Britain. They are not usually pure stands but have oak, ash, hawthorn, elder and rowan intermingled with the dominant birches. These provide a varied and nutritious diet. Woodlands dominated by birch, however, tend to be more open and have a less impressive field layer. This allows birds such as the yellowhammer and the willow warbler to nest in fairly high densities. There are also 'specialists', such as the tree pipit and willow tits.

Tree pipit *Anthus trivialis*
The tree pipit finds isolated trees ideal posts from which the male launches himself into the air and to which he returns at the conclusion of his parachuting song routine. The open ground between the trees so typical of birch scrub is exploited as nest sites. The food of

this migrant species consists mainly of insects and their larvae which abound in the soft timber of birch. In recent times the tree pipit has extended its range despite some loss of habitat in marginal areas around towns. The increased planting of conifers by the Forestry Commission may have been partly responsible since many birds are able to utilise the scrubby seedling stage. It is interesting to note that the tree pipit does not breed in Ireland, although it may have done so in the past. According to Dr J. T. R. Sharrock, this may well be due to the almost total removal of woodland in Ireland during the eighteenth and nineteenth centuries. There is every chance that recent extensive plantings may encourage the species to return.

Redpoll *Acanthis flammea*
The redpoll has shown a startling population increase in recent years and can now be found in almost any type of woodland. They are especially fond of birch, the seeds of which form the bulk of their winter diet. Only 12·5 centimetres (5 inches) long, both sexes of this little finch are a warm brown above with a few darker streaks whilst the belly and flanks are lighter but still streaked. The bill is strong, but the feature which makes identification easy is the crimson forehead and small black chin patch. The untidy grassy nest is often sited in birch and in it a clutch of four or five eggs are incubated for about eleven days. The young are able to fly within a fortnight.

Willow tit *Parus montanus*
At 11·5 centimetres (4½ inches), the willow tit is the same size as the marsh tit but the black crown is dull and not glossy. The two are, however, very difficult to separate physically and it is more reliable, as with the warblers, to rely on variations in song. The marsh tit has a loud 'pitchew' call and the willow tit has an easily recognised buzzing 'zurr-zurr-zurr'. This species is also able to excavate its own breeding hole, providing the timber is soft enough, and it thus finds birch ideal. Despite its susceptibility to fungal attack, birch can often act as a pioneer tree, preparing the ground for ash and for oak. In deep fertile soils the dominance of oak may

Tree pipit (**top**) and willow tit (**bottom**).

be challenged by beech, a condition found naturally in Britain only in the south-east. Whenever small plantations of beech occur, however, the specialist birds quickly move in.

Birds of beech wood

A typical beech woodland has a very close canopy due to the masses of small but intermingling deep-green leaves which create heavy shade and prevent growth in the layers below. Even when the leaves do fall they decay so slowly that only a few specialised flowers and fungi can grow among them. Researches by W. B. Yapp and by E. Simms, among others, list the breeding birds, including chaffinch, blackbird, woodpigeon, wren, robin, great tit, willow warbler and occasionally woodpeckers. The two species normally associated with a beech wood in winter are the closely related species the chaffinch and the brambling.

Chaffinch *Fringilla coelebs*
The handsome male is 15 centimetres (6 inches) long, has a blue head, a delicate chestnut-pink flush on his cheeks and a black forehead. His chest is rosy-red and the wings are brown but with yellowish white wing bars and a white shoulder patch. There are also two white marginal tail feathers which like the wing markings are very prominent in flight. The female is smaller and duller but both have the powerful bill typical of the finches. In winter the flocks tend to be either predominantly male or female, and this accounts for the bird's specific name of *coelebs*, which means bachelor. This seems to be due

The chaffinch – a common resident in Britain.

to the males having a greater migratory urge than their mates and it has the advantage of leaving the females with enough to eat in times of winter shortage without having to overcome the rigours imposed by long journeys. The chaffinch is one of Britain's most successful species and a breeding population of about 7 million birds has been estimated. Despite having its origins in deciduous woodlands, *Fringilla coelebs* has adapted well to the changes wrought by human activities and its vernacular name of chaffinch derives from its habit of scouring the harvest fields at the time of plenty.

Brambling *Fringilla montifringilla*
The brambling is often called the northern finch, taking over from the chaffinch in the birch woods of northern Europe. Breeding records in Britain are few and far between but in winter they often come south in large numbers in search of beechmast, one of their

Brambling cock — bramblings are frequent
winter visitors to Britain.

favourite foods. Bramblings closely resemble chaffinches but can be distinguished by the white rumps of both sexes, whilst the male also has an orange-coloured shoulder patch.

Despite the quite impressive array of British woodland birds discussed in this chapter we are but poorly furnished compared with the splendour of some continental woods. As we have seen, the ice ages had some effect, but the richness of the continental avifauna also reflects their better conservation record. Before the advent of man in Britain some 60% of our land had tree cover. By Norman times (according to the Domesday Book) this had been reduced to 20% and by 1918 to below 5%. We must not assume that the forest area was solid woodland for lightning would cause fires and produce natural clearings which would be kept clear by grazing animals such as deer, which would be attracted to the warmth of the sun-drenched areas and prevent seedlings from growing and thus healing the wound. The 1914–18 war belatedly made politicians aware of the timber shortage and this resulted in the setting up of the Forestry Commission with the job of putting matters to rights. With the understandable wish to increase the area of marketable timber, the trend was towards the planting of quick-growing conifers. This has led to the Commission coming under frequent and heavy fire from some conservationists whose arguments, although partly true, do represent extreme rather than informed opinion. It is said that there has been a failure to plant any hard-woods, and that conifer woods are devoid of wildlife. The first statement is not quite true and in any case valuable work done by the Nature Conservancy Council, the Woodland Trust, Men of the Trees and the county naturalists' trusts (see p. 203 for addresses) has increased the planting of hard-woods. The second point concerning a total lack of wild-life associated with coniferous woodlands is even more misleading, as I hope the second chapter of this book will prove.

2 Coniferous Woodlands

'There is nothing in a conifer wood and so there is no point in going into one.' This statement was, and still is, frequently uttered by naturalists in general and ornithologists in particular, who also describe conifer plantations as alien monocultures which are as much of a threat to the natural history of Britain as herbicides and pollution. Is this condemnation fair? In the light of recent work it would seem not. Britain has always had her own Caledonian forest dominated by our native conifer, the Scots pine (*Pinus sylvestris*), and this is not only rich in wildlife but also supports some species such as the capercaillie, the crested tit and the Scottish pine crossbill which do not occur anywhere else in Britain. Not enough naturalists went into the 'foreign forests' to enable them to refute the suggestion that only chaffinches, woodpigeons, coal tits and the odd demented or disoriented goldcrest ventured into the cold dark interiors. It must be admitted that the situation was polarised not only by ornithologists but also by the Forestry Commission itself which in its early days often discouraged visitors. This attitude has changed dramatically in the past few years and naturalists have been pleasantly surprised at both the variety and the populations of birds in the conifer forests.

Indeed, there is some evidence to suggest that the modern conifer industry may bestow some advantages on birds since the trees are harvested on a 40- to 80-year cycle. This means that there will be periods when scrub dominates and this is suitable for ground-nesting birds such as short-eared owls, grey partridges, grasshopper warblers and yellow-hammers; and, if there are any taller trees left dotted around, tree pipits may well use them as song posts. It is an essential part of the forester's work to trim off the lower branches. If these are left lying they make good scrub habitat and if they are burned the sites of the bonfires may be gladly accepted by nightjars in search of nest sites. The hen harrier, which went through a difficult time in the 1960s, is now making a spectacular comeback partly as a result of a reduction in the use of pesticides and partly because of a more realistic attitude towards birds of prey by most, but regrettably not all, sections of society. The importance of conifer plantations in their early stages should never be under-estimated, and birds of coniferous areas may therefore conveniently be divided into two groups: first, the birds present in the ancient forests of Scots pine; and, second, those which are learning to live and thrive in the newer plantations.

The pine forests of Scotland

Apart from juniper and yew, the Scots pine is the only coniferous tree native to Britain. Some 9,000 years ago it grew throughout these islands but after this time the climate began to change and wetter, warmer conditions prevailed. This situation favoured the growth of alder, lime and oak, but some relict pine populations still thrived in areas such as the Cambridgeshire fens, where the relatively dry surfaces on top of raised bogs provided good habitat. The real splendour of these ancient pine forests and the varied life forms they supported survived only in the Highlands of Scotland. It has been estimated that the Great Wood of Caledon spread over 3 million acres and wolves roamed free, wild boars scraped among the debris of the woodland floor, wild cats growled from their lairs, black cocks 'lekked' in the clearings and capercaillies took off with the clatter of their down-curved wings echoing throughout the forest. Where is the Great Wood of Caledon now? Thanks to a lethal combination of

Yellowhammers nest among coniferous scrub and in other open areas with low ground cover.

The staring eyes of the young short-eared owl deters predators.

climatic change and human thoughtlessness, it has been reduced to a series of still vulnerable remnants at places such as the Black Wood of Rannoch, Beinn Eighe on the west coast, and the still impressive Rothiemurchus Forest, curled up under the shelter of the magnificent Cairngorms.

In view of the damage inflicted upon the southern woodlands we might well wonder why this huge northern wonder survived as long as it did. Hadrian had his legions build their wall to keep the Picts and Scots in their forests, the Saxons were far too busy hunting beasts and bashing each other to worry about the pagans of the north and the pines were safe – until the arrival of the Vikings, whose thirst for timber for fires and ships began to chip away at the Great Wood of Caledon. This was, so to speak, the thin end of the wedge, and as the English sought to oust the Scots from their native land the forests were an obvious refuge for the outlawed Highlander. A policy of burning these areas was therefore eagerly pursued and the final nail in the pine woods' coffin came after the 1715 and 1745 rebellions, when the now impoverished clan chiefs were heavily fined by the lackeys of the Hanoverians. They had only one asset which could be turned into cash – timber. Down came the forests of pine and with the mighty trees went the native mammals. Many of the birds also suffered in the days when the intricate and delicate ecological balance was understood even less than it is today.

In the ancient forest the pine was able to regenerate, but in recent years it has lost this essential ability. Part of the problem would seem to be that the undergrowth is far too thick for the seedlings to be able to penetrate on their own and they really need animals such as the wild boar, reindeer and elk, each of which in its search for food turned over the ground rather like a plough and thus allowed light to reach seedling pines. Birds such as the crossbill still play their role of scattering the seed, but the animals which dug them in have long since vanished. It is quite clear that human activities have upset the balance but it also seems that at this most crucial time in the life of the pine forest the fickle climate is beginning to exert a powerful influence. As the warmer, wetter weather raises the water table, sphagnum moss develops and functions rather like a gigantic sponge. I was once in the heart of Rothiemurchus with a group of fellow naturalists in June with the highland weather at its notorious worst. Rain fell steadily from low grey clouds, wind howled off the top of Cairngorm, and we were glad of the shelter offered by the pines. Every footstep brought water welling up over our boots as we trod on a soaked blanket of the sphagnum sponge. In one area the moss was even thicker than usual and the wind had toppled over twenty fine pines whose roots had been no longer able to find firm ground to anchor themselves against the gale tugging and pushing at their upper branches. Thus sphagnum can accelerate the destruction of what is left of the Great Wood of Caledon and we must hope that the facts now accumulated by ecologists from the Nature Conservancy Council and other bodies will be enough to prevent the death rattle of the pine. It is yet another reminder that the only way to save rare birds – or any living organism, for that matter – is to preserve the habitat, beginning with the plant life on which all depend.

When considering the bird life of these native pine forests we have to bear in mind that there has been so much felling by man and grazing by sheep that they are better considered as wooded heaths rather than forests as such. This is not altogether a bad thing from an ornithological point of view as the clearings allow birds such as meadow pipits and yellowhammers a niche which would not have been available to them in the good old days. In these open spaces other species which would normally have been shaded out by the pines are able to grow, including alders (especially where burns trickle though the glens), rowan, aspen and especially birch and juniper. These ensure food and shelter for such bird species as fieldfare, redwing, siskin and several species of tit. An under-storey of heather and bilberry can also thrive here and provide ideal conditions for short-eared owls, hen harriers and black grouse. In addition to these uncommon but fairly widely distributed species the

Sparrow-hawk in aggressive posture at nest.

Opposite (above)
Hen harrier nestlings in defensive posture.

Opposite (below)
The redpoll (**left**) and the siskin (**right**) are frequent winter visitors among coniferous woodlands.

Scottish pine woods also contain birds which are not found in other areas of Britain. These are the capercaillie, the crested tit and the Scottish pine crossbill. There can be no doubt that during the last century these remnants of forest have provided a refuge for predatory birds which would otherwise have fallen to the wiles of the gamekeepers anxious to please their wealthy employers by keeping gibbets full of birds with hooked bills and mammals with fangs. Birds which have so benefited include the osprey and the sparrow-hawk. Thus to represent the ornithological treasures of the pine woods we will describe the life-styles of the capercaillie, the black grouse, the crested tit, the crossbill and the osprey before going on to discuss other species which occur in the recently created forestry plantations.

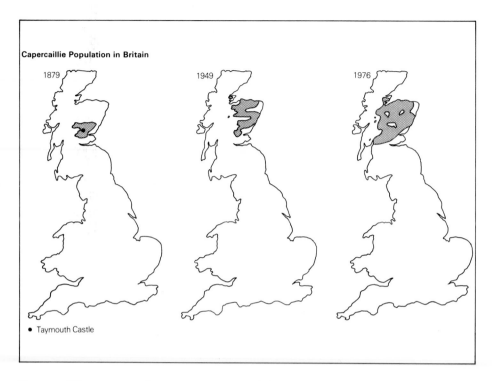

Capercaillie Population in Britain

1879

1949

1976

● Taymouth Castle

Capercaillie *Tetrao urogallus*

The native pine forest had been reduced to such pitiful proportions that by 1770 this wonderful bird, the name of which derives from the Gaelic, meaning old man of the woods, was extinct. What a pity to have lost this often awe-inspiring creature. The females are 60 centimetres (2 feet) long and the males a massive 90 centimetres (3 feet), with a wing span in excess of 120 centimetres (4 feet). The cock 'caper' has a plumage of dark slaty grey with flecks of white on his body, but the throat and sides of the head are black and there are areas on the breast which are green and flash greeny-black. Over the eye is a smooth patch of bright red. The bill is dirty white but looks brighter in contrast with the dark plumage. Finally, a straggled 'beard' of greenish-black feathers can often be seen and may well have been the reason for his name of old man of the woods. The female is much browner and speckled, thus leading to confusion with the grouse. With experience, however, the hen capercaillie can be distinguished from the grouse by a reddish patch on her breast and her larger size. The

duller plumage obviously enables her to sit tight on the eggs. The capercaillie normally flees from intruding humans but there are records of Scottish cocks defending their territory with considerable gusto. One infamous bird laid claim to a small wood in Angus over a period of four years and attacked sheep and people (including ornithological photographers of impeccable pedigrees) with beak and claw and was more than a match for the lot of them.

The loss of such a magnificent species was obviously a tragedy, especially to those who could remember hunting it; in 1827 Swedish birds were released on Deeside but the scheme failed. In 1837, however, a successful re-establishment programme was initiated by Lord Breadalbane, who brought thirteen cocks and nineteen hens over from Sweden to his estate at Taymouth Castle near Aberfeldy. From this estate the capercaillie spread and encouraged further introductions, the spread being indicated in Maps 1, 2 and 3 which were produced by reference to the work of Tim Lovell (see below). Johnston and Zwickel found that in the Black Wood of Rannoch the

The male capercaillie can be very fierce in defence of his territory.

breeding density was about one bird for every 5 or 6 hectares (1 hectare = about 2½ acres). At present the breeding population is below 10,000 pairs. Increased planting of conifers should ensure their survival, but the capercaillie is still pretty much restricted with only the occasional straggler reaching the western Highlands. The work of Lovell suggests that it will not be long before capercaillies occur regularly in these western outposts. The first arrivals seem almost always to be females and the shortage of cock birds has occasionally resulted in hybrids with blackcocks and even with pheasants. The resultant offspring are sterile and once the cock capercaillies arrive the hybrids cease.

Searching for breeding capers involves a visit to a suitable habitat and listening for the unique and almost indescribable song, if such it can be called. On a cold, crisp, calm morning in April I made my way into a typical Tayside woodland and thought about the sound I had been told to expect. 'It's like a champagne cork going pop,' said one expert. 'No, it's like the grinding of a knife,' replied another, whilst a third compared it to 'heavy breathing'. This latter description coupled with what I had read about the aggressiveness of the odd cock bird in Scotland added an extra dimension to the chilled atmosphere of the early morning. In the event I saw my bird before I heard him. He was perched on the flat top of a stunted pine close to a small clearing. He drooped his wings, lifted his head and fluffed out his neck feathers, and began a most bizarre dance, during which he behaved as if the foliage was red hot. As he jumped up and down he began to 'pop' and I could see the reason for the champagne analogy as one pop followed another in rapid succession – what a party! A croaking from the ground below drew my attention to a group of four hens who obviously liked his particular vintage. Beyond the clearing another party was in full swing as a rival male emptied his cellar of vintage pops, and like my close neighbour successfully mated with each of the assembled hens. Some days later, also at dawn, I witnessed two males competing with each other for the favours of three hens and the popping was fast and furious. On this occasion they stood and snarled at each other and one phrase used repeatedly was very like 'heavy breathing'.

It is hardly surprising that the male pays no attention to the nest and eggs since he may well be the father of several clutches. The hen chooses a nest site usually at the base of a pine tree, although there are some sites among heather or among juniper. Five to eight pale-yellow eggs marked with dark brown are laid in late April on a lining of pine needles, moss and occasional feathers. They hatch after about a month. The chicks leave the nest as soon as they are dry, their subsequent development is very rapid, and they are able to flutter along the ground in just over a fortnight. They are, of course, very vulnerable at this stage and this is why it is important that all the eggs should hatch at the same time. Thus the hen can gather all her flock around her and not have to wait around for late arrivals. The communal breeding grounds also ensure that the hens lay their eggs around the same time and produce some protection from the safety of numbers. Thus the 'lek' system is useful. The word 'lek' is Norse in origin and means to play. In the northern areas of Britain the phrase 'laking about' is still frequently used.

Lekking is also typical behaviour of another threatened game bird which also has some of its remaining refuges in the pine woods of Scotland. This is the black grouse, and like the capercaillie it is thought to have evolved thousands of years ago in eastern Siberia, which then had short hot summers when insect life abounded and enabled the young to mature quickly before the long winters closed in and left only the pine needles to keep the birds alive.

Black grouse *Lyrurus tetrix*

The black grouse is certainly faced with the threat of extinction in Europe and in a fascinating article published in *Country-Side* in summer 1983 Dr Tim Lovell, Chairman of the World Pheasant Association, outlined the decline in the status of the species over the last century in Europe in general and Great Britain in particular (see Maps 4, 5 and 6). There does, however, seem to be some disagreement among ornithologists regarding the present status of the black grouse. The total breeding population in Britain is thought to be between 10,000 and 50,000 pairs, but if we pause to consider what these figures actually mean we can appreciate that there is a huge difference between the lower and the higher limits. One view is that the species is widely distributed in Scotland and the northern Pennines, with reasonable populations in other areas, for example in Wales, in the Peak District and on Exmoor. It is admitted that there was a serious decline during the nineteenth century but that a significant rise in population and perhaps also distribution has occurred since. However, this is not the view of Tim Lovell, who in his *Country-Side* article observed:

'In England a hundred years ago it inhabited most of the uncultivated heathlands and must have been extremely common. Even eighty years ago it was said to be found in every county south of the Thames, with the possible exception of Kent. The maps give some idea of its decline. It is now found only in two tiny scattered remnants on Exmoor and Dartmoor, small numbers exist in Wales and Staffordshire, and only when one reaches North Yorkshire and Durham do the numbers resemble anything like their old strength. In Denmark the decline has been even more dramatic: 80 years ago 50% of Jutland was heath: this proportion has now

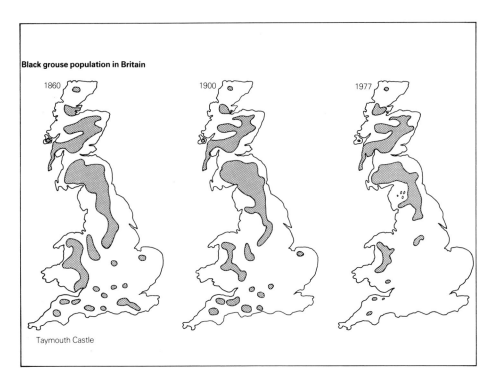

Black grouse population in Britain

1860

1900

1977

Taymouth Castle

fallen to 9%. The black grouse population has fallen equally, and in the last 40 years has dropped from 2,500 birds to 100, scattered over 10 separate relict populations. In Holland and Belgium too there is only a tiny population left. In West Germany it has been greatly reduced, and is now a protected species. Only in Scandinavia and in Scotland are the numbers still substantial.'

There can be no doubt that the black grouse is a species well worth preserving (which species is not?) and to achieve this, areas of pine forest and open moorland with the lush shoots of heather need to be preserved. For some reason blackgame has never been reared and released, but it is still shot in the season which begins on August 20th and ends on December 10th. Outside this season of slaughter they have the full protection of the law. It does require a long and detailed inquiry to discover if the optimists are correct in assuming that, despite shooting pressure, the population is rising. I, like Tim Lovell, believe that the reverse is true and that there is a case for extending the period of protection

to cover the whole year. We cannot afford to lose one of our most beautiful birds for we have few sights to compare with a blackcock in full breeding regalia.

When viewed from a distance through a moorland's morning mist or in the clearing of an evergreen wood the blackcock earns his name, but when struck by the slanting rays of the springtime sun this splendid fellow, about the same size as a domestic hen, plus his long tail, takes on a lovely steely-blue gloss. His white wing bars and elbow joints, known as 'headlamps', are clearly seen. I well remember on one occasion in Derbyshire and on another near to Kindrogan Field Centre in Perthshire watching small groups of springtime black-cocks lekking as dawn crept up slowly over the hills. The strutting dancers curled their tail feathers to form a lyre shape which they vibrated, and produced a semaphore of white flashes from the underside of their coverts; over each eye a scarlet wattle gleamed like a ruby in the sun. But by July the wedding dress begins to fade and some of the tail and flight feathers are lost, which makes the once proud blackcock prefer to sulk in the depths of the

The black grouse has special breeding grounds called leks.

forest rather than draw attention to himself as he loves to do on the lekking grounds.

The female, called the greyhen, is a much less spectacular bird and not seen as often as her mate. This, of course, is the object of nature's exercise just as it is in the case of the capercaillie.

Fluctuations in blackgame populations have been noted by natural historians in previous centuries. The Forestry Commission are convinced that their new plantations in areas such as Ashdown in Sussex, the New Forest and Thetford Chase will allow black grouse to increase but in truth the species is not too particular about its habitat and can manage to survive on heather moorland, cultivated fields, and uplands heavily grazed by sheep, as well as in birch and conifer woods. What it does require is peace and quiet in order to complete its breeding cycle, beginning with the springtime leks, followed by the laying of six to ten eggs which invariably takes place during the first couple of weeks in May. The nest is often situated among heather under trees but there are occasional records of old

crows' nests high up in the pine trees being used by adventurous greyhens, which makes us wonder how the young get down from these heights. The eggs seem to be laid on alternate days and take between 24 and 28 days to hatch, the precise time seemingly dependent upon temperature. The eggs are yellowish but are liberally spotted, streaked and occasionally blotched with brown. The chicks are covered in a delicate yellow down but with darker feathers on the back. As with the capercaillie, the young, which feed on protein-rich insects, mature rapidly and the majority take their first tentative flight during their third week. It may well be that the forester ought to welcome the presence of breeding blackcock in the area since they do contribute something at this stage of their lives to the control of potential insect pests. In the winter, however, the birds' diet can sometimes be worrying and Jenkins estimates that up to 80% of leader shoots can be damaged by birds feasting on the fresh buds of pine and larch. This can be particularly worrying in the first two years of a new

Coal tit.

plantation when the shoots can be nipped by blackcocks standing on the ground and systematically grazing through the area. A great deal more work is needed, however, before the blackcock can be branded as a pest with any certainty and destroyed as such, a move which has been advocated by some soulless extremists. It is a clear example of the need to weigh carefully the minor damage caused by a particular species against the aesthetic advantages of its presence.

It is not only the two large game birds which make a visit to the Scots pine forests a memorable experience, for over eighty species of bird have been known to breed within them, although it is often the additional presence of a loch or burn which creates sufficient diversity to attract them. Two titmice are very much a feature of a pine wood, namely the acrobatic coal tit and the delightfully engaging crested tit. Where they occur together the former species outnumbers the latter by almost 4 to 1, and is much more adaptable in its choice of nesting site, even being prepared to accept crevices among

stones and undergrowth. The crested tit demands soft decaying tree stumps and such sites are a feature of a mixed-aged ecologically balanced pine wood, but not of a mono-culture of disease-free uniformly aged alien plantations. Thus crested tits are not usually a feature of the Scandinavian avifauna.

Coal tit *Parus ater*
The coal tit can be distinguished from the rest of the family by a clearly defined white patch at the nape of the neck which stands out against the black cap and the species also has a narrow white double wing bar. The bill of the coal tit is narrower and slightly longer than is usual in the tits and this means that it can hunt for food among the needle-like leaves of conifers. It can thus exploit an ecological niche not available to the more aggressive great tit or the more acrobatic and resourceful blue tits. Up to one million pairs of coal tits may breed in Britain, the nest being con-structed by the female from moss and lined with lichen or hair and perhaps the occasional feather. She appears to build mostly during

The crested tit – increasingly common in Scotland's pine forests.

the mornings and although she will accept nest boxes she prefers natural cavities in timber. There are also many instances of the burrows of rodents such as the bank vole or short-tailed field voles being usurped. During nest building the male stays close to the female but falls short of physically helping. One egg is laid on successive days but incubation does not commence until the clutch, which varies from seven to eleven eggs, is complete. There are occasional clutches of pure white eggs but they are usually speckled with reddish brown. Incubation, which takes between 10 and 14 days, again dependent upon temperature, is the responsibility of the female but she is fed and protected by the attentive male. Coal tits are early breeders and in mild springs eggs may be in the nest before April is out.

Crested tit *Parus cristatus*

It is quite accurate to describe the coal tit as a true coniferous bird, but it is the crested tit, of which about 1,000 pairs are found in Britain,

which typifies the ancient pine woods with their open glades full of bilberry and heather. The Spey valley is the main area for the crested tit, which is the only European member of the family which has a crest and is thus easy to identify. The sexes are not easy to distinguish, but some workers have suggested that the females have slightly shorter crests than the males, although this is a statistical difference rather than a valuable distinction in the field. In addition to the crest both species have a line of black running round the neck so that a collar is formed and where these join they widen to form a small bib. There are no strikingly white facial patches which are so much a feature of the other titmice, but during display the crest may well function so effectively that such patches are not necessary. In any event the species is easily recognised by the bird watcher and it is also a good species for the bird listener. High up in the pine branches they are more often heard than seen and the 'tzee-tzee-tzee' notes are typical and easy to recognise with just a little practice. The fact that they prefer the company of their own species rather than form mixed flocks is a further distinction between the crested and other members of the tit family.

Some workers have suggested that crested tits do not have a song, but this is only because it is high-pitched and often delivered from high perches where it may be difficult for the human ear to detect over the creaking branches and the sighing of the wind. The song must work since the female is drawn towards the male and then she sets about excavating a nest hole in a dead or decaying tree – another feature which is not typical of the titmouse family. It is an example of parallel evolution in that the crested tit not only behaves like a woodpecker in excavating its nest but can also feed like one at times, as it digs out insects trapped in the sticky sap oozing from the peck marks in the tree trunk.

Within the nest, which is lined with moss, wool and hair, six white eggs, spotted with red, are laid and incubated for two weeks by the female alone, though she is fed regularly by her mate. Once the eggs have hatched both parents feed the young which may require as long as three weeks' continuous attention before they fly. With very rare exceptions only one brood is produced. Thus family groups can remain together and a feature of the relict pine woods in late summer is their tzee-tzee-tzeeing through the branches. There seems to have been some element of competition for a suitable niche between the crested tit and the coal tit which has been sorted out to their mutual benefit by the former species feeding on the trunk and the larger branches whilst the latter are found on the outer branches. The crested tit appears to be very stationary and unless really atrocious weather drives them to bird tables and picnic sites they remain in their woods. This tendency to remain in one place is almost, but not quite, typical of the crossbill family, which is still evolving rapidly.

Scottish crossbill *Loxia scotica*
This bird is still causing some confusion among taxonomists and its scientific name has been altered several times in recent years.

Crossbills are members of the finch family, about 16·5 centimetres (6½ inches) long. They have heavy and uniquely shaped bills, ideal for extracting seeds from conifer cones. Crossbills afford an ideal opportunity for ornithologists to observe evolution in action because they can be divided into obvious geographical races by the varying sizes and shapes of the bill which have evolved in response to the particular diet. In all races the upper and lower mandibles cross over, making the bill look deformed. Usually crossbills do not move very far from their native forests but every so often the seed crop fails and the hungry birds 'irrupt' in search of food. An irruption is most likely to happen when a prolific cone year is followed by a poor harvest and the increased population comes under real pressure. These irruptions have been faithfully recorded in ecclesiastical history because it was believed that the crossed bills were caused by the bird's unsuccessful attempt to remove the nails when Christ was suffering on the cross. Similarly the reddish plumage of the cock was due to his being splashed with blood. The males are really attractive creatures and the crimson stands out clearly from the black on the wings and the tail. The hen is olive-yellow and if it was not for the crossed bill she could be mistaken for a greenfinch. She does, however, have the dark wings typical of the male.

The common, also called the red, crossbill (*Loxia curvirostra*) breeds all around the northern hemisphere where there are pine forests and the similar parrot crossbill (*Loxia pyropsittacus*) breeds in the pine forests of Scandinavia, the Baltic and northern Russia. Northern Russia also has a population of the two-barred crossbill whilst Siberia and Canada also have this species. The precise status of crossbills in Scotland has been the subject of fierce debate but it is now generally accepted that the Scottish crossbill is a distinct species, having a much heavier bill than the European species. The population in the old pine forests is therefore thought to have evolved from the parrot crossbill and not from the European crossbill. Some 5,000 breeding pairs may occur, the majority being resident *Loxia scotica*.

The crossbill – an irruptive species, common in some years and uncommon in others.

Following an irruption some common crossbills may remain in Britain and these isolated pockets may survive and breed for several years before dying out. No breeding has been recorded in Ireland. Whilst crossbills may feed in dense forests they prefer to build the untidy twiggy nest close to a ride or a clearing. The male is never far away from the female but he does little, if any, of the work. It is also the hen who incubates the four eggs, during which time she is fed by the attentive cock. She cannot afford to leave the eggs since crossbills breed early in the year – the occasional clutch may even be laid in December – and the young also reveal an incredible resistance to cold. They appear to be able to enter a state of suspended animation almost akin to hibernation, a phenomenon which has been studied in more detail in young swifts. After about a week young crossbills begin to maintain a constant body temperature. Another peculiar feature is that the chicks have straight bills which only gradually grow crooked and finally cross. At first the male brings crushed and regurgitated seeds and passes them on to the female who feeds the young, but once they can hold their body temperature steady both parents feed them. This can be no easy task since it has been estimated that each may require over 3,000 seeds per day. They may not be fully independent of the parents until they are in their fifth week. Watching crossbills is a most rewarding experience, but it has to be worked for because although the birds are not all shy they tend to feed high in the branches of the pines and their presence is indicated only by the 'jip-jip-jip' of their call and the descent of fragments of pine cone discarded as the birds rip them apart to get at the seeds.

Typical birds of the new plantations

Long-eared owls have increased because more conifer plantations are now maturing and providing nest sites.

It was while having my breakfast and being bombarded with bits of pine cone descending from a visiting flock of European crossbills which had irrupted into a new plantation in north-western England that I had my most exciting day as a bird watcher. Through a break in the larches I could see an osprey fishing in the reservoir, and a long-eared owl flew past me on its way to roost. As if this wasn't enough to persuade me of the value of the plantation the real gem revealed itself in the form of a goshawk. It is thought that both the goshawk and that other rarity the firecrest may be increasing, and the lovely little goldcrest may also be expanding its range because of these ornithologically underrated areas.

Goshawk – a species becoming more common as coniferous plantations mature.

Goshawk *Accipiter gentilis*

The goshawk demands several essential factors before it can breed successfully. Two of the most important are an expanse of forest and freedom from disturbance. I am fairly certain that the silence factor is of greater importance than the nature of the habitat and the goshawk breeding population now exceeds sixty pairs. The main increase occurred during the 1970s and a levelling out took place during the early 1980s. This suggests that the increase

may have had more to do with the deliberate release of imported goshawks and recently implemented quarantine regulations may have slowed this process. As it resembles an overgrown sparrow-hawk, gamekeepers tend to view the goshawk as a sort of mobile slaughterhouse and over fifty birds are known to have been killed by keepers; despite laws to prevent it many still use the barbarous poletraps as well as highly dangerous poisons.

Accipiter gentilis varies in length from 47 to

57·5 centimetres (19–23 inches) and has a long tail and rounded wings. The male is smaller than his mate but, unlike the case of the sparrow-hawk, the sexes look alike. They are dark ashy-brown above and the occasional bird has a distinctly blue cast on its plumage. A clearly visible streak runs from the eye to the ear coverts. The underparts are pale but finely barred in dark brown and the tail is very obviously barred. The under-tail coverts are white and show up well in flight. The diet of the goshawk differs from that of the sparrow-hawk (another example of the ecological niche) in that it takes more mammals and its greater size brings many birds too large to be tackled regularly by sparrow-hawks directly into the danger zone. Its favoured habitat is a forest overlooking an open moor and thus many of the new forestry plantations have proved to be ideal for the introduction of goshawks. The female takes almost all the responsibility for the construction of the huge nest of twigs, sited in a tree. Three or four eggs are laid in April or May. Incubation, again dominated by the female, takes around 37 days but once the young hatch the male plays his full part in feeding the young, which can fly around 40 days after hatching.

Firecrest *Regulus ignicapillus*
Big is not always beautiful and, although it is a tiny bird, the presence of a firecrest in a woodland creates as much interest as the mighty goshawk – if not more. In May 1976 the following note written by Leo Batten appeared in the *Newsletter* of the British Trust for Ornithology.

'In view of the continuing spread of Firecrests in this country, a full scale enquiry into their breeding distribution and habitat preferences may possibly be launched in 1977. Singing birds have been recorded in the breeding season as far west as Gwent and as far north as Yorkshire, so it would be no great surprise to hear of breeding birds from any suitable habitat in Britain. A survey of this rather elusive species poses several problems and the purpose of this note is to help in finding Firecrests.

The searcher must be familiar with the Firecrest's song. The call notes are harsher than those of the Goldcrest, sounding more like zit-zit-zit than the si-si-si of the more common species. However, the difference is not so marked when the first broods of young Goldcrests are on the wing as their calls tend to be more strident than those of the adults. Efficient and productive searching can be aided by the use of a tape recording of the song. This usually elicits a response from Firecrests holding territory, although it is sometimes necessary to play the tape for several minutes. Firecrest territories may be over half a hectare in size and as the bird may be a hundred metres away from the recorder it can take a time for the bird to hear and then locate the position of the sound source . . . . Most Firecrests arrive on their breeding grounds from early to mid-May and the best time to locate them is from then to mid-June. Playing taped Firecrest song will stimulate birds to sing up to mid-July. The most productive time of day for locating birds is early to mid-morning.

A wide range of habitats are now known to be used by Firecrests in this country. In approximate apparent order of preference these are: mature or semi-mature Norway spruce, Douglas fir, Scots pine, Larch, Western hemlock (all at least 25 ft high), Yew and Beech, mature Oak with Holly, Oak, Birch and Holly. On the Continent, Firecrests are found in a variety of woodland types and one generally considers them to be more catholic in their choice of habitats than the Goldcrest, a habit which is now becoming more apparent in this country.'

This census was certainly necessary because following the discovery of a breeding pair in the New Forest in 1962 several other counties were thought to have resident firecrests and the range is known to be expanding. Populations are, however, erratic and Eric Simms has recorded forty-three singing males in one area alone. I have observed firecrests in Yorkshire, southern Scotland, Lancashire, Wales and of course the New Forest. This species shares with the goldcrest the honour of being Britain's smallest bird. It measures only 7·5 centimetres (3 inches) and weighs

Gold crest (**left**) and firecrest (**right**).
Note the position of the eye stripes – goldcrest
above the eye, firecrest through the eye.

a modest 5 grams. This means that it takes almost six of them to make up an ounce. The next time you buy a quarter of sweets hold them in your hand and you have the combined weight of twenty-four firecrests. The equally tiny goldcrest is no heavier. The two species can be distinguished by the fact that the firecrest lives up to its name and its crest is also more extensive than that of the goldcrest. There is also a conspicuous white superciliary band and a black stripe through the eye-line. It remains to be seen whether the forestry plantations will allow the increases to continue, but it has been suggested that the diet of spiders and insects may not enable the firecrest to survive a hard British winter. The goldcrest, although it is affected in really long cold spells, has a similar diet. If the firecrest ever did become numerous the two species might well begin to compete for the same ecological niche. What is needed here is a detailed comparative study but work already done on the continent would seem to suggest that the goldcrest is much more dependent upon conifers than the firecrest.

Goldcrest *Regulus regulus*

The goldcrest was formerly known as the golden-crested wren, a family to which the species is not related. At 8–9 centimetres (3–3½ inches) it shares with the firecrest the distinction of being our smallest breeding bird. The fine bill distinguishes it immediately from the tits and reveals the close affinity to the warbler family. Males can be distinguished from the females by the orange centre to the yellow crest – a feature which sometimes leads to confusion with the firecrest. The food consists mainly of spiders and insects and this diet must mean great hardship during bad winters, although some insects do show a remarkable power to survive the cold due to presence of ethylene glycol (antifreeze) in the blood. A walk through a conifer wood will often disturb goldcrests which loop from the top of one tree to the next calling 'zi-zi-zi' quite loudly. Most of the vocabulary, however, is high-pitched, quiet and difficult to hear, although young ornithologists can usually pick up the notes better than their elders. The nest is a wonderfully mossy structure suspended by handles from beneath a conifer bough and both sexes beaver away at the structure. Only the female incubates the seven to eleven red-spotted white eggs laid on a soft lining of feathers. The young emerge after just over a fortnight. The male then takes up his duties and helps in the feeding. Within 24 days the young can fly and a second brood is usually raised.

There is no doubt that goldcrests typify a conifer wood but after a series of mild winters and successful breeding seasons the population may be high enough to allow expansion into deciduous woodland. There is also a great deal of movement during the spring and autumn migrations and at this time the coastal bird observatories may be inundated with goldcrests from northern Europe where the winters are tough. It is to these coastal areas that we turn in the next chapter, and in this habitat wildfowl and waders are much more typical than the passerines.

3 The Coast

In Chapter 2 the threats to our native pine woods were considered. At the other extreme we find that there are problems at sea level just as there are in the upland forests. Whenever a river flows towards the sea it carries with it debris collected along its journey and this includes useful nutrients as well as potentially dangerous chemicals. As the river slows down as it reaches sea level, the heavier materials can no longer be supported and they fall out to form muddy silt. Sooner or later the river meets the sea, which is carrying its own load of debris in the opposite direction. When the force of the tide is equal to the strength of the river current, the two cancel each other out and even light particles are deposited. Here then, is an estuary, which is usually an expanse of miles of mud-flats full of invertebrate life with the landward aspect developing into botanically rich salt-marshes. Both mud-flats and salt-marshes are wholly or partially inundated by the tide twice each day, clearing away the debris or, perhaps it would be more accurate to say, moving it to another beach. Add to this the sand-dunes which sometimes fringe the estuary and you have a perfect environment for birds.

Unfortunately the point where a river reaches the sea is the most sensible spot to construct a commercial port. This brings with it great benefits to the human population but also the dangers of pollution – oil refineries, gas pipelines, chemical complexes. The increasing human populations mean the production of large volumes of untreated sewage. Because this latter form of pollution is aesthetically undesirable, especially around the holiday resorts, its effect has often been overstated. Untreated sewage, as long as there is not too much of it, adds nitrates, phosphates and other valuable chemicals to the seawater and when broken down this allows more animals and plants to survive. The breakdown of sewage does make demands on

the oxygen and if there is too much sewage the levels of oxygen fall, the animals cannot breathe and there is a real pollution problem. This seldom happens in Britain's seas and there is plenty of evidence to suggest that the Thames estuary, Morecambe Bay and the Firth of Forth may have benefited from sewage if judged by the state of their wildlife rather than on the opinion of well dressed and carefully manicured holidaymakers. Two sea ducks have certainly increased their numbers around the sewage outlets from Edinburgh; now these outfalls have recently been controlled a corresponding drop in populations is likely.

Goldeneye *Bucephala clangula*

Although there are frequent records of goldeneyes spending the winter on inland waters they prefer sheltered bays and often huddle in flocks in sheltered bays and estuaries. *Bucephala* means 'ox-head', and the shape of the goldeneye's bill and forehead is certainly unique. Post-mortems reveal a large air space situated behind the nostrils and connected with the sinuses. This accounts for the unusual shape, but what function does it have? It certainly provides an extra reservoir when the bird dives for its food, which consists of mussels, crabs, worms and the occasional fish found in shallow water. On the other hand the reservoir is so large that the buoyancy which it gives could reduce diving efficiency. It has also been suggested that the reservoir is smaller in males than in females but there is no reason why this should be so. It could be another example of each sex having a separate ecological niche – the male's comparative lack of buoyancy allowing him to go deeper whilst the female's extra load of air allows her longer to search for food in shallower and perhaps muddier water. As with all ducks the difference between the sexes – 'sexual dimorphision' – is pronounced. The underneath of the body of the male is basically white, which contrasts sharply with the darker back streaked with neat lines of white and the dark head which, when it reflects sunlight, has a lovely greenish sheen. A large round white spot on the cheek identifies the drake goldeneye at almost any distance and even in poor light. Both sexes have the bright golden eye from which their vernacular name derives, but the female is of a brownish grey, darkening on the back, and the head is the colour of milk chocolate. Goldeneyes are about 45 centimetres (18 inches) long, the females being rather smaller. They are showing an increasing tendency to breed in the British Isles. They prefer holes high up in trees and will even take to nest boxes. The female, now deserted by her once attentive mate, incubates her clutch of 7–14 bluish-green eggs for about four weeks. Once hatched, the young are obliged to scramble out of the nest and jump before following the

duck to water. The family remain together for about sixty days, by which time the young can fly. Goldeneyes tend to be solitary nesters, in complete contrast to another estuary-based sea duck, the eider.

Eider *Somateria mollissima*
Eiders are northerly distributed ducks which, over the last century, have been expanding both in population and distribution. There may be as many as 2 million birds wintering in Europe alone and the breeding colonies are now appearing further south and substantial numbers are now found in Northumberland and Cumbria. I have studied the colony at Walney Island in Cumbria and watched it grow from a solitary nest in 1949 to over 800 in 1983. There are few finer sights than a male eider in his full breeding plumage and in earnest pursuit of a mate. Both sexes are Roman-nosed, the bill coming straight down from the forehead with no angular structure typical of other ducks. Apart from making the eider easy to identify, this feature gives the species a rather aristocratic appearance. The

Female eider incubating – eider-down provides the perfect insulation for developing eggs.

male's appearance does nothing to detract from this impression. His underparts are black and the rest of the body snow-white but with a delicate green on the back of the head and a flush of pink on the breast. The breeding male eider does look the part. The duller female is of a rusty brown with darker dappling. The scientific name *Somateria mollissima* means 'soft-body of wool', which is an ideal description. The down with which the duck insulates her nest has been sought by northern tribes since before written history began and we still have the word 'eiderdown', while the French name for the species is 'eider à duvet' (shortened to 'duvet' in the vernacular).

The eider is a good mother and her clutch of eggs is usually covered with down on the few occasions when she leaves them during the month-long incubation period. If she is flushed from the eggs she sprays them on her departure with evil-smelling excreta; this often deters predators, which suggests that the sense of smell may well be more important in the lives of birds than has often been realised. Once the eggs have hatched the dark-coloured ducklings have to be taken to the sea since wildfowl do not feed their young. The eider colonies are often situated close to, or actually within, gull colonies and the babies are literally sitting ducks unless some strategies are evolved to ensure their safety. At 59 centimetres (23 inches) and very power-fully built, the female eider can protect herself easily and so she keeps her young close to her body and when the hungry gulls come into attack she sits on her offspring and remains there until the gulls get tired of waiting and seek another target. Once the young reach the sea several clutches may be gathered together and the whole crèche defended by a group of females. This method has proved much more successful than the trust-to-luck technique employed by other species which breed along the shores and estuaries. Included here are shelducks, red-breasted mergansers, mallards, ringed plovers and oystercatchers.

Waders

The estuaries provide a vital nesting habitat, but it is in the colder months of the year that British estuaries come into their own and provide food and shelter for millions of waders. If our estuaries were too polluted, or, as has been suggested, barraged to produce extra water for wasteful industries, these birds would literally have nowhere else to go and many would face imminent extinction. Estuaries in winter are full of waders, which in America are perhaps better described as shore birds. The order of birds called the Charadriiformes (which also includes gulls, terns and auks, which will be described in Chapter 4) has a suborder named the *charadrii*, or waders. Two families (almost 200 species) make up this suborder, namely the plovers (*charadriidae*) and the sandpipers (*scolopacidae*). Plovers are relatively small birds, usually within the range 15–40 centimetres (6–16 inches). The legs are usually short and their bill length is almost always shorter than the head length. As befits short legs and bills they usually feed by picking and pulling at prey on the mud rather than wading in and digging, which is much more typical of the long-billed, long-legged sandpipers. Thus once more we can see how the range of feeding niches operates to give the ducks the chance to feed when the sea covers the mud and rocks; when the water ebbs birds of the sandpiper group, typified by the curlew, take their fill; and on the mud flats and along the strand line the ringed plover can obtain its share of nature's bounty. During the early 1970s many estuaries were either heavily polluted or threatened with some sort of development and the British Trust for Ornithology conducted an inquiry to discover which species were using which estuaries and at what time of the year were they reliant upon them. Tables 1 and 2 summarise these findings.

Curlew *Numenius arquata*

At 55 centimetres (22 inches) the curlew is Britain's largest wader and its tall spindly legs, long curving bill and streaked brown plumage make it easily identifiable. Apprentice bird watchers, however, especially when looking over a winter estuary with wind and sleet blowing in their faces, do not always find it easy to distinguish between the curlew and our two species of godwit. In the spring when

<table>
<tr><td colspan="2">

TABLE 1

Top twenty estuaries for waders in Britain and Ireland

</td></tr>
</table>

Estuary	Peak count
Morecambe Bay	234,000
Wash	177,000
Solway Firth	165,000
Dee	136,000
Ribble	133,000
Severn	72,000
Firth of Forth	66,000
Humber	56,000
Shannon/Fergus	56,000
Burry Inlet	40,000
Dundalk Bay	40,000
Strangford Lough	38,000
Lindisfarne	34,000
Foulness	31,000
Chichester Harbour	30,000
Duddon	29,000
North Bull	28,000
Langstone Harbour	27,000
Blackwater/Dengie	25,000
Swale	24,000

Figures based on BTO survey

TABLE 2

The highest monthly total of waders counted on British estuaries, 1970–3

	Highest count	Month of highest count
Dunlin	550,000	January
Knot	350,000	January
Oystercatcher	200,000	September and January
Lapwing	110,000	January
Redshank	103,000	September
Curlew	66,000	September
Golden plover	55,000	January
Bar-tailed godwit	43,000	January
Sanderling	26,000	May
Ringed plover	25,000	August
Turnstone	13,000	January
Grey plover	8,000	February
Black-tailed godwit	5,300	September

Figures based on BTO survey

Possibly a relaxation in shooting or perhaps subtle climatic changes have resulted in a substantial increase in the number of curlews nesting in Britain and the population is certainly more than 45,000 and may be approaching 80,000 breeding pairs. Four eggs are laid during April or May in a scrape in the ground, usually near a clump of grass or sedge, and both parents incubate them for a period of about thirty days. As with the crossbill, the bills of the young are straight and only develop their downward curve towards the end of the six-week fledging period. It seems that curlews do vary somewhat in size, between 48 and 58 centimetres (19 and 22 inches). The birds with the longest bills are invariably females. By the end of July the curlews will have made their way to the beaches and estuaries and may join the godwits already there.

the whimbrel is passing through they have a fourth species to add to their identification difficulties. Table 3 should make these problems less difficult.

The curlew is the only one of these four species which regularly breeds in Britain and in mild winters they may leave the comparative warmth of the estuaries for the hills and dales where their bubbling calls and graceful display flight tell the people of those parts that spring is on its way long before they hear the call of the cuckoo or the first swallow surveys the barns in search of a nest site.

TABLE 3

A comparison of the larger British waders

Species	Head and body size	Bill size and shape	Length of leg and colour	Status in Britain	Distinguishing features
Curlew (*Numenius arquata*)	55 cm (22 inches)	Average 12·5 cm (5 in.). Down-curved. Females all have the longest bills.	Greenish-grey. 8·5 cm (3·4 in.). Female slightly larger.	Common breeder. About 55,000 pairs.	A white rump but not sharply defined from the white tail.
Whimbrel (*Numenius phaeopus*)	40 cm (16 inches)	Average 8 cm (3½ in.). Down-curve not so pronounced as in the curlew.	Greenish-grey. 6 cm (2–4 in.). Sexes the same.	Not very common. A passage migrant which breeds in Shetland and the Outer Hebrides and occasionally St Kilda. Less than 250 pairs.	Two broad dark bands on the crown. This is lacking in the curlew. The whimbrel is more easily approached than the curlew.
Bar-tailed godwit (*Limosa lapponica*)	35 cm (14–15 inches)	Pinkish. 7½ to 10 cm (3–4 in.). More upcurved than black-tailed godwit.	Grey. 5·5 cm (2·2 in.). Females slightly longer.	Fairly common winter visitor. No breeding.	The tail is white but there is a very prominent subterminal black bar.
Black-tailed godwit (*Limosa limosa*)	40 cm (16 inches)	Pink shading to black. 11·3 cm (4½ in.). More or less straight.	Greenish-black legs look rather short for the body. 8 cm (3·3 in.). Males slightly longer.	Winter visitor but not so common as the bar-tailed. A few breed in Britain (less than 90 pairs), but the numbers are increasing.	Broad white wing bar makes it easily distinguishable from the bar-tailed. Legs project well beyond tail in flight. The tail is black.

Above
The curlew breeds on the uplands and winters on the coast.

Below
Whimbrel – a relative of the curlew, but rare in Britain.

Black-tailed godwit (left) and bar-tailed godwit (right).

Black-tailed godwit *(Limosa limosa)* and Bar-tailed godwit *(Limosa lapponica)*

Godwits can be identified by their long, straight or even slightly upturned bills and slimmer figures. They are, however, often overlooked and are usually undercounted.

The black-tailed godwit is about 40 centimetres (16 inches) long and the bill extends a further 10 centimetres (4 inches) beyond this. Immediately it takes to the air a white wing bar, a striking black-and-white tail and the habit of trailing its long legs beyond its tail distinguish the black-tail from its near relative the bar-tailed godwit, which is a much darker bird. When both species are on the ground and in winter plumage, however, they are difficult to separate. In summer the black-tail has a very extensive patch of chestnut on the breast and after being 'lost' as a breeding bird in Britain it has now returned to East Anglia and northern Scotland. It has also shown signs of summer-ing regularly close to many estuaries and may soon decide to breed close by. It still occurs more frequently in winter but its numbers never approach those of the bar-tailed godwit, which, however, shows no sign of breeding. A glance at Table 2 will show the relative abundance of the two. The bar-tailed godwit is 2½ centimetres (1 inch) shorter than the black-tailed, it has comparatively shorter legs, and the bill shows a quite definite tendency to turn upwards. In flight a clearly visible white rump, the complete lack of a wing bar, a stouter shape and a barred grey tail make identification easy. It spends a great deal of its time feeding on sandy and muddy shores in the company of curlews, redshanks, dunlins and knots. The differences in leg length, bill size and shape enable each species to tap the habitat's food supply at a different level – in other words each bird has its own ecological niche and once more the bird and its habitat are in perfect accord.

Two other waders, at the other end of the size scale, which are often confused by apprentice

Above
Redshanks breed on the moors and spend the winter on coastal marshes.

Below
Greenshank — although only a few of these waders breed in Britain, many pass through on migration and use our marshy areas as feeding stations.

Dunlin (summer) – a few pairs of dunlin remain in Britain to breed.

bird watchers are the knot and the dunlin, the two most numerous species found in British estuaries (see Table 2).

Dunlin *Calidris alpina*

Known in North America as the red-backed sandpiper, the dunlin is Europe's most common wader. At one time it seems that the whole population bred just to the south of the ice during the time of the last ice age when most of Britain was frozen. All but a relic of the population have followed the ice to breed in the cooler areas. This wader is 17·5 centimetres (7 inches) long and has a fairly long down-curved bill. It is, in fact, the bill which has given ornithologists something to think about. During the great ice movements many separate populations of dunlins became isolated, and interbreeding produced a series of races. The birds found in the most northerly parts of the range tend to have smaller bills relative to the body size. Obviously the smaller the bill the less heat will be lost and here we have yet another example of how birds adapt to their environment.

Those dunlin which do remain to breed in Britain – between 4,000 and 8,000 pairs – are found mainly on high wet moors, with just a few pairs choosing to try their luck on the salt-marshes. One of the most delightful features of dunlins at this time is the sweeping but graceful display flight of the males. As there is often a tendency for several pairs to breed close together the naturalist with a stout heart and a good pair of lungs may reap a fair reward for the slog to the boggy heights of a moorland. It is chilly in the hills and it is often towards the end of May before four eggs are laid and incubated by both parents for around three weeks. As with all waders, the young are active almost as soon as they are dry. The parents feed them almost continuously until, after 25 days, the young can fly well enough to accompany them to the estuaries, where they will soon be joined by the migrants of the species and also by large numbers of knot.

Knot *Calidris canutus*

Knot are characterised by their complex flight patterns when hundreds, and sometimes thousands, of birds fly together. The twisting and turning is perfectly synchronised. The whole flock, with reflexes almost beyond belief, turn as one and then at a given signal land and begin feeding. It is then that the stocky grey-and-white knot can be seen to be larger than the dunlin – it is 25 centimetres (10 inches) long. The legs are shorter and the bill is also shorter and straighter than that of the dunlin and a further distinction can be seen when the birds fly. The tail of the knot is a uniform colour and not dark in the centre and paler at the sides, as the dunlin's is. By far the best areas for watching both knot and dunlin are the estuaries of north-western England between the Solway and the Dee, with Morecambe Bay supporting the most impressive numbers. If this area were ever barraged, or polluted by atomic waste from the long established Windscale nuclear power station or the one being constructed at Heysham, these waders would be hard pressed to survive in Europe. There are populations on the Humber and in the Wash but compared with populations in north-western England they are relatively small. One other threat has recently come to the forefront. Oil and natural gas have both been discovered in and

off Morecambe Bay, almost certainly in commercial quantity, and if these are gathered carelessly the waders could be in real trouble.

I was once asked to investigate the effect of the huge influx of holidaymakers to the west coast resorts on the natural history, with particular reference to the bird life. Imagine the author with binoculars slung around his neck weaving his way through the 'Kiss me Quick' hats, bathing belles and fat fellas to count the birds. What did emerge is that there are areas where birds can feed in peace and holidaymakers do not carry guns. There is literally safety in numbers and as waders feed on the mud after the tide has gone out they can gorge themselves in comfort whilst humans bask on the sand. Add to this the English climate, when many days are not suitable for swimming, and the fact that early morning tides are not popular, and the true pattern emerges. Waders and people can live together in peace, and in the main neither worries about the other.

The ruff is another wader that winters in Britain. A few pairs now breed here, each male displaying a unique and extravagant variation of plumage. The female is called a reeve.

Above
The red-necked phalarope, a rare visitor to Britain found among saltmarsh pools, can be recognised even from a distance by its habit of turning in a circle whilst feeding on plankton stirred up in shallow coastal water.

Below
The turnstone turns over weeds and stones, thus taking advantage of a unique feeding niche.

Sanderling *Calidris alba*

Sanderlings, which reach a peak in Britain during May and again in July, also bear witness to this: the most popular place in Britain for this very pale dumpy little wader, which is about 20 centimetres (8 inches) long, is the area between St Annes pier and Squires Gate Airport at Blackpool. In flight the sanderling has a very prominent wing bar, and it displays an even more typical piece of behaviour when feeding close to the sea. It runs in with a receding wave and grabs a morsel of food before running out in front of the next wave, looking for all the world like a clockwork toy. On beaches which are full of rocks and seaweeds, purple sandpipers and turnstones also seem well able to cope with holidaymakers.

This situation certainly does not apply to other species and three in particular have suffered greatly from our increased leisure, which means that we now tend to intrude into their habitat at a crucial time. These three species are the oystercatcher, the ringed plover and the little tern.

Oystercatcher *Haematopus ostralegus*

With its clear black-and-white plumage, its red bill and legs and its large size (43 centimetres or 17 inches), the oystercatcher is one of the most numerous and conspicuous birds found on the coast. Between 25,000 and 40,000 pairs nest in Britain but the winter population is much greater than this. Whilst the sight of the sea-pie, as the species used to be called, is a delight it is really the lovely 'kleep-kleep' call sound which, to me, is most typical. Many is the night I have spent on the shores of Morecambe Bay huddled among the dunes and well insulated against the cold, listening to the pies and watching them feed by moonlight. They are often joined by flocks of redshanks and a few solitary hunch-backed grey plovers, but because of differences in bill and leg length there is little if any competition between them. In fact the name 'oyster-catcher' is one of the most misleading in the ornithological world, because oysters figure seldom if ever in their diet. They are mainly cockle eaters and because of this are not at all popular with commercially minded cockle gatherers. Which came first – man or bird? Judging by the way it splits the bivalve shell it is obvious that the bird is the master of its art – and the powerful bill can bash open cockles and mussels so that they are very quickly anything but alive, alive – o! This must put some stress on the bill, but nature has solved this for the oystercatcher by providing it with a bill which, unlike that of most birds, grows throughout its life. The oystercatcher can also cope well with a diet of worms since, like many waders, it can open the tip of its bill independently of the rest of the organ, so that underground prey can be held without the mouth being opened.

The typical nest site of the oystercatcher is on a shingle beach, the precise habitat favoured by increasing numbers of beach anglers. We need, say the economists, to be educated in the use of leisure time. What better answer is there than to spend the day catching the evening's supper with perhaps enough left to barter with a neighbour for a bottle or two of his home brew? This harmless hobby can interfere with the successful breeding of coastal birds like the oyster-catcher. During the month-long hatching period, the female, who does most of the incubating, must sit on her eggs and the presence of a fisherman will not allow her the necessary privacy. He who fishes in the heat of the day will not know that the eggs of the oystercatchers who constantly buzz around him are boiling in the sun. He who fishes in the cool of the night will not know that the unincubated eggs have dead embryos within them. Once the young are hatched they are well camouflaged and will probably survive, but many never reach that stage, because of the innocent fisherman enjoying his hobby. Some species, such as the little tern, have been unable to survive this pressure, which is even greater in the areas given over to holiday and caravan complexes, and are showing clear signs of becoming extinct as breeding birds in Britain. Indeed, the whole tern family is very sensitive to disturbance (see Table 4 and Chapter 4).

Both the oystercatcher and to some extent the ringed plover have solved the problem by moving up the rivers and nesting on their

TABLE 4

British breeding terns

English name	Scientific name	Size	Bill colour	Leg colour	Status and distribution
Common tern	*Sterna hirundo*	33·5 cm (13 in.)	Red, usually with a black tip	Red	Summer visitor arriving April and departing late October. About 15,000 pairs breeding. Breeding centres include Farnes, Scillies, Anglesey, Thames Valley, Blakeney Point.
Arctic tern	*Sterna paradisaea*	35 cm (14 in.)	Blood-red, usually without black tip	Red. Legs shorter than common tern	Summer visitor mid-April until late October. About 30,000 breeding pairs, the majority in Scotland, but also at Portland-Chesil Beach, Walney, Foulney, Anglesey, Coquet. Largest English colony is on the Farnes (3,000+ pairs).
Roseate tern	*Sterna dougallii*	35 cm (14 in.)	Black with perhaps just a little red at the base	Red	Summer visitor arriving late April to mid-September. Population now less than 2,000 pairs, and declining sharply. Found around Firth of Forth, Firth of Clyde (Horse Island), Anglesey, the Scillies, Farnes, and an important colony of Coquet Island.
Sandwich tern	*Sterna sandvicensis*	40 cm (16 in.)	Black with yellow tip	Black and long for a tern	Note the prominent crest. Summer visitor from late March to September. About 10,000 pairs, sites including Scolt Head, Minsmere, Havergate, Ravenglass, the Farnes and the Firth of Forth.
Little tern	*Sterna albifrons*	25 cm (10 in.)	Yellow with black tip	Yellow	Less than 2,000 pairs and declining. Summer visitor from May to September. Colonies at Blakeney, Scolt Head, Cley, Dungeness, Anglesey, Walney, Rye Harbour, Inner and Outer Hebrides.

The ringed plover – a common seashore resident.

shingle banks. The oystercatcher has done this for some considerable time in Scotland but in recent years there has been successful breeding at the heads of both the Lune and the Ribble, as well as in the Trough of Bowland. The oystercatcher in these areas seems to have become a cow-clap catcher and eats large numbers of beetles and other insects feeding on the dung, as well as wireworms, earthworms and caterpillars.

Ringed plover *Charadrius hiaticula*

In my home county of Cumbria the ringed plover is affectionately known as the stone-runner and this exactly describes its tendency to run away from danger in preference to the more conspicuous use of flight, since it blends in perfectly with the sand and shingle. Although only about 20 centimetres (8 inches) long this little bird more than makes up for its lack of size by its engaging character. The black collar from which it gets its vernacular name can be seen from a distance as can its orange legs and short orange bill with a black tip. Until recently it was not possible to confuse this species with any other but in recent years the little ringed plover has

begun to breed in a few inland sites in Britain and a comparison of the two is given in Chapter 9. Probably no more than 6,000 pairs breed in Britain, and habitat losses discussed above may be causing it problems. It is to be hoped that it adapts to its new, somewhat experimental, inland niche as efficiently as the oystercatcher, which has pioneered the route. Although the chase-and-display routine begins as early as February it is April or perhaps May when the first of the four eggs are laid in scrape, usually on shingle. Both sexes share the period of incubation, which can take as long as 26 days, but I have observed two nests in which the period was 22 days. In these exposed habitats external temperatures do vary a lot but I have a feeling that the two short periods occurred in nests on uninhabited Scottish islands where there was no disturbance – I could see the nest from my boat and through a telescope. Both sexes look after the young, which can fly after about 25 days. This leaves time for a second brood, and in a good summer a third may well be attempted.

Shelduck *Tadorna tadorna*

This chapter has taken the form of an imaginary journey from the open sea, over the exposed mud-flats and onto the shingle

The shelduck — one of the most attractive
British wildfowl.

fringes of the estuary itself. If we continue
inland we shall meet one or two more species
which occupy the sand-dunes and salt-
marshes. Included here will be the gulls,
which are described at length in the next
chapter, and the terns, already briefly
mentioned. Two birds, the shelduck and the
stonechat, typify a Maytime sand-dune, and as
I write they bring back memories of spring
mornings spent watching the sun lift the last
wisp of mist from the dune slacks lined with
yellow flag among which the rare natterjack
toads breed. A shelduck, unaware that her
nest site is no longer unknown, creeps away
from her nest deep in a rabbit burrow and
walks out to her mate feeding on the mud-
flats. Her secret is safe with me. Often the sun
strikes a patch of marram grass on the crest of
a dune. Here, bathed in the early warmth, is
the second species to grace this particular
habitat – the stonechat. The shelduck, with
its loud 'ak-ak-ak' call, occurs all around the
coast of Britain where reasonably quiet and
flat sandy beaches occur. There are fewer than
a few years ago but the breeding population is
still between 10,000 and 15,000 pairs. The
winter population has been estimated to be
around 50,000. The shelduck is a reasonably
easy bird to census as it feeds on the open

shore, choosing shallow pools left by the
ebbing tide, which are rich in marine worms,
crustaceans and molluscs, especially the tiny
snail *Hydrobia* which more than makes up for
its lack of size by its astronomical populations. The shelduck is not likely to be
confused with any other species, and although
there is a variation in size from 60 to 66
centimetres (24–26 inches) the colour
patterning is spectacular. The basic pattern is
black and white but the bright orange band
round the shoulder can be seen clearly at a
distance. It is only from close quarters or in
bright sunlight that the dark green head looks
anything other than black. The male tends to
be larger than the female and has a prominent
knob at the base of the red bill.

Courting parties gather as early as January
and by March the pairs begin to prospect for
suitable sites in the dunes, often being prepared to chase out resident rabbits. Hollows
beneath trees or sometimes marram grass
roots are also popular sites, but its alternative
name of burrow duck clearly indicates the
female's preference for extensive holes in the
sand.

Several aspects of the shelduck are not
typical of ducks in general. It is very unusual
in ducks for the sexes to look alike, while this
is typical of geese and swans. Some taxonomists have even suggested that shelducks
should not be classified as a duck, a swan, or a

goose, but should be given a category of its own.

Female shelducks can lay a clutch of up to sixteen eggs but nests have sometimes been found with more than twenty eggs in them. This is due to a couple of females sharing the nest, although one female is usually very much the boss. After about a month the eggs hatch, all the incubation having been carried out by the female. The male stays close to his mate. Again we find that this behaviour is more typical of geese and swans than of ducks. Immediately after hatching the young are led to water and a crèche system may operate during the couple of months it takes for the

birds to fledge. During July and August the flocks begin to increase, and then the bulk of the British population sets off on migration to the shallow Heligoland Bight area, where they are joined by shelducks from the rest of Europe. It would seem that there is safety in numbers and the moulting masses give mutual protection from predators. In recent years it has been noticed that a few thousand Irish birds moult in Bridgwater Bay, Somerset, and other smaller moult migration flocks may be developing on the Wash and the Firth of Forth. The return from the moult begins in late autumn and the birds are back on the breeding grounds by January.

It is remarkable how often nature seems to be able to defy logic. A tough species like the shelduck would seem to have little need for

The stonechat is common on the coast and occasionally breeds inland among the gorse.

any form of migration, whereas its fellow dune breeder the stonechat would seem to be an ideal candidate for migration and yet it chooses to sit out the winter and remain on the dunes throughout the year.

Stonechat *Saxicola torquata*
The stonechat is a tough, dumpy robin-like little bird measuring about 12·5 centimetres (5 inches). It is not restricted to coastal habitats, but sometimes overlaps with that of the whinchat on inland moors and heaths. The migratory whinchat (*Saxicola rubetra*) can always be distinguished from its resident cousin by the presence of a very prominent eyestripe which is lacking in the stonechat.

The favoured breeding habitat for the 30,000 to 60,000 pairs of British stonechats is the coastal flat lands, especially where gorse predominates. After a good breeding year in these districts the species may extend its range by some birds moving inland. During a bad winter the population may crash dramatically, but the slightly higher temperatures due to the salty air around the coast allow the breeding reservoir to survive and the trend begins again. Stonechats under pressure resort to foraging along the strand line, where the piles of stinking, rotting vegetation generate heat and therefore support good populations of insects, crustaceans and worms on which the hungry birds feed.

By March the male with his shining black head and back, chestnut breast and pale rump is standing erect on marram, curled dock or gorse branch, chat-chat-chatting his claim to territory. Periodically he will rise into the air and then flutter rather clumsily back down to earth in an effort to attract the dull brown and speckled female. She builds the nest of grass lined with hair and feathers in the shady confines of a gorse or bramble patch. The hen also takes the major share of the two-week incubation period required by the five or six greenish eggs. Both parents feed the young, which develop quickly and vacate the nest in about a fortnight, leaving the parents to begin a second brood.

Although other passerines are found breeding on the dunes – including linnets, skylarks, meadow pipits and cuckoos – it is the stonechat which to me is the typical passerine of this habitat. The sand-dune naturalist will find much of interest whatever the season, but the view from the crest of a sandhill over the sea offers a chance to watch seabirds and it is at these times, especially after gale-force winds, that really rare species may be spotted. Many seabirds have their breeding sites threatened by man's industrial and leisure activities but the highways of the sea remain open and in Chapter 4 I will describe seabirds in general and European species in particular.

4 The Sea

The casual visitor to the coast cannot fail to be aware of the seabirds which are a vital part of our marine fauna, as well as the coastal waders and wildfowl which were discussed in Chapter 3. When the ornithologist talks of birds such as waders, wildfowl, warblers, woodpeckers, crows or thrushes we know that a scientifically defined list of birds is meant. This is not the case with seabirds – a very loose title indeed. They cannot, however, be ignored as a group since of all the habitats discussed in this book the problems posed for birds ranging the oceans are by far the most demanding from both a physical and a physiological point of view. Some understanding of these difficulties can be gained by considering seabirds from three viewpoints: first we will examine how they are classified and how the various families have evolved methods of adjusting to their environment; then we will consider the biological innovations which enable them to live on and around sea water; finally, we shall evaluate the greatest threat to seabirds – that posed by human activities.

Classification of seabirds

There are just over 8,600 species of bird alive today belonging to 28 orders but distributed very unevenly over the world's surface. Despite the fact that more than 70% of the planet is covered by sea there are, depending upon the authority consulted, only between 260 and 285 accepted species of seabird and all are included in one of only four orders. The situation has been summarised in Table 5.

The Penguins

The penguins are totally restricted to the southern hemisphere but it is wrong to assume that all eighteen species are restricted to polar regions, for many birds occur in Australia, South Africa and South American regions. What they do require, however, is plankton-rich cold water such as that provided by the Humboldt current which allows the Galapagos penguin to thrive within a degree or two of the equator just off the coast of Ecuador. Although penguins are now flightless there is plenty of anatomical evidence to suggest that their ancestors were flighted. The breast-bone has a prominent keel to which are attached powerful muscles which now drive the 'flippers' to such good effect that some penguins can reach speeds of up to 12 knots. Controlling heat loss from the body is achieved partly by the overlapping feathers, which also serve the equally important function of keeping the surface of the skin dry. Penguins also have a thick layer of

TABLE 5

Simplified classification of the world's seabirds

Order	Family	Number of species
Sphenisciformes	Penguins	18
Procellariiformes	Albatrosses	13
	Petrels and shearwaters	61
	Storm petrels	18–22
	Diving petrels	4
Pelecaniformes	Pelicans	7 (only 1 is marine)
	Gannets and boobies	6–7
	Cormorants	30
	Frigate birds	5
	Tropic birds	3
Charadriiformes	Gulls	44
	Terns	39
	Skuas (also called jaegers)	6
	Auks	22
	Skimmers	3
	Total	277

blubbery fat just beneath the skin and indeed the name derives from the word *pinguis*, meaning fat. The family is in quite a healthy state at the moment and most species are increasing despite, as we shall see later, rising levels of pollution. Some scientists are of the opinion that the wholesale slaughter of whales has led to a substantial increase in the populations of planktonic crustaceans (collectively termed krill) and that populations of penguins could rise even more dramatically to take advantage of this man-created bonanza. As a naturalist I think I would prefer nature to balance her own books.

The Procellariiformes

These include the thirteen species of albatross. They are naturally restricted to the southern hemisphere, although a few fossilised remains have been uncovered at North Atlantic sites. It seems certain that all the seabird families had their origins south of the equator and have spread gradually north from these regions. The albatrosses, however, are basically gliding birds and individuals have seldom managed to penetrate the area of calm known as the doldrums. There is no doubt that some species are able to survive in North Atlantic areas: for example, the black-browed albatross has occurred several times in British waters. One individual lived among the gannets of the Faroes between the years 1860 and 1894, another was well documented during its stay on the Bass Rock gannetry between 1967 and 1973, and from the late 1970s to the time of writing a third individual – perhaps the same bird – seems to be thriving around the Shetlands.

The order as a whole is very pelagic, spending the whole time at sea apart from when breeding. The typical 'tube nose' structure seen so well in the fulmar, but present in all members of the order, has had many hypothetical functions ascribed to it, including its use as a sort of telescopic sighting device used in catching prey. Recent work, however, seems to point to the tube functioning either as a mechanism for judging wind speed during gliding or as an organ of smell. Ornithologists, sensibly in my view,

are rapidly moving away from the opinion that birds make little or no use of the sense of smell, basing their evidence on dissections of the brain which often reveal large olfactory lobes.

The petrels and shearwaters constitute a large family known technically as the *Procellariidae* and can be conveniently divided into six groups. First, there are six rather heavily constructed species called fulmars, five of which are concentrated in the higher latitudes of the southern hemisphere whilst the sixth is the so-called northern fulmar which occurs in the North Pacific, North Atlantic and increasingly around the coasts of Britain. The species has been the subject of a great deal of research in recent years (stimulated initially by the works of James Fisher) because of its remarkable increase in both range and population. It has been discovered that no fulmar remains have yet been discovered in prehistoric middens while remains of great auk, gannet, kittiwake and storm petrel have been found. It seems likely that they had reached the island group of St Kilda by the ninth century, but I think that it is safe to assume that the fulmar did not become really common there until the nineteenth century. It was at this time that the St Kildans switched their 'economy' from total dependence on the gannet to a partial but increasing dependence upon the fulmar. Having spent some time on St Kilda counting both species, I can say with certainty that the nests of the fulmar which are centred on the main island of Hirta are much easier to reach than those of the gannet, which are concentrated on the two great stacks of Lee and on Armin. It is logical to assume that the St Kildans began to farm the fulmar immediately it became common enough.

The next point which demands an answer is the reason for this population explosion. During 1969–70 a census was attempted of all seabird colonies and 'Operation Seafarer', as it has become known, calculated the population to be 306,000 pairs and rising at the rate of about 7% per annum. Clearly this needs to be explained and one of the most plausible views came from Wynn-Edwards. He suggested that some genetic change, possibly even

Fulmar incubating — the fulmar uses jets of oil as a defence mechanism.

within one individual, produced a sort of 'super-fulmar' which was able to cope more easily than its peers with the harsh marine conditions. Providing that this dominant gene was retained, the fulmar's offspring would be bound to be successful. The Finn, Salmonsen, agreed with Wynn-Edwards up to a point but suggested that a small group of fulmars, possibly as a result of genetic change, began to move south following a cold current and found a rich area of planktonic food with no competitors already in possession of the niche. James Fisher, in total contrast, suggested during the 1950s and early 1960s that it was as a direct result of man's activity that the fulmar had suddenly become successful. Initially, he argued, the whaling industry and then the fishing fleets were in the habit of flensing and gutting their catches at sea and the amount of offal thus made available to the pelagic fulmar would be sufficient to keep alive a large number of birds which would otherwise have found difficulties surviving in a purely natural environment. Fisher further argued that the population explosion had slowed down by the mid-1950s and this coincided with the demise of the whaling industry and the tendency of refrigerated fishing fleets to process their offal for pet foods or fertiliser. Scientific

arguments, like all others, tend to become polarised and Fisher's reasoning does not account for the increased populations of fulmars in areas where fishing or whaling has not been common practice and in any case the population increases are still continuing. Offal has, however, been a contributory factor in many areas but there may well have been a genetic change and the species has certainly taken advantage of cold currents to spread south, a factor well-documented by Brown, who worked with James Fisher and sensibly noticed the increased volume of plankton (the fulmar's natural food) in cooler waters. The fulmar is another ideal example to illustrate the theme of this book, which is to show how birds can adapt themselves to extract the maximum advantage from their chosen but ever-changing environment.

Prions

Prions are the second group of the *Procellariidae*. They have proved difficult to classify but there are probably 12 species concentrated around sub-Atlantic islands where they select crevices or burrows as nest sites.

A manx shearwater incubates its single egg in its burrow.

They show an interesting adaptation of bill structure to enable them to feed upon marine zoo-plankton by sieving water through a series of comb-like structures called *lamellae*. They drive water through the *lamellae* by swimming quickly forwards with their bills open.

Gadfly petrels

The gadfly petrels have suffered greatly as a result of human activities. The Pterodroma cahow found around Bermuda was once very common but the colonies were preyed upon both for food and sport by mariners and early settlers to such an extent that the species was regarded as extinct. After several irregular and often unconfirmed sightings a breeding population was discovered but the cahow population is still hovering dangerously close to extinction. The cahow, as you would expect from a species on the brink of extinction, is vulnerable to any form of pollution and chemicals such as DDT and dieldrin have certainly had some adverse effect upon its recovery. A very recent discovery is of another member of the family, the magenta petrel of the Chatham Islands, which may have a population of only about twenty birds – yet another example of how we can affect the fortunes of birds.

Shearwaters

The shearwater group, which range the seas and move with ease from one hemisphere to another, have suffered from the effects of widespread oceanic pollution. One really phenomenal journey is undertaken by the short-tailed shearwater which from its nest on islands off the south-eastern coast of Australia can make a figure-of-eight migration via Japan and Alaska before looping back to the breeding grounds which it reaches in September. The total length of the journey is in the order of 32,000 kilometres (20,000 miles) and is achieved by an almost uncanny use of the prevailing winds.

The shearwater family have also been shown to possess quite remarkable powers of navigation plus a very strong homing instinct – features highlighted in Ronald Lockley's

Storm petrel.

classical study on the Manx shearwater. On the island of Skokholm, Lockley worked with David Lack, and the two of them transported nesting adult shearwaters several hundred miles from the island before releasing some birds over the sea and others at inland locations. Two birds were released out of their normal range at Venice on the Adriatic but were able to return to their nests within a fortnight. The experiment was extended and Lockley and Lack found that given a clear sky Manx shearwaters thus transported, or should it be transplanted, anywhere in western Europe chose the correct heading almost immediately after their release. Four individuals with eggs or chicks to look after or a mate to return to were sent by aircraft to Boston, Massachusetts. Two birds homed in on their nest burrows, one after an absence of 12½ days, the other 36 hours later. They had flown a straight distance of about 4,080 kilometres (3,050 miles) thus averaging 320 kilometres (200 miles) per day.

Most authorities accept that there are eight definable races of the Manx shearwater of which the nominate race with clearly defined black-and-white plumage breeds along the west coast of Britain with small colonies also found in the Faeroes and the Westmann Islands off Iceland. Ringing returns have shown a winter movement to the coasts of Brazil and Argentina. The adults return to Europe as early as January when they make their way to the Inner Bight of the Bay of Biscay, where they feast on rich stocks of sardines. If this supply ever declined then the Manx shearwater population would reflect this change very quickly. Birds incubating the single egg or tending a chick in the deep dark tunnels of Skokholm may occasionally make a journey of 960 kilometres (600 miles) each way to have a feed, leaving the partner to carry the burden of the domestic chores. As spring gives way to summer the journey is not so demanding, for young sardines, now known as pilchards, spawn in the English Channel. As the pilchards return to the Bay of Biscay, they are predictably followed by the Manx shearwaters, which are thus showing perfect adaptation to their environment.

Storm petrels
The storm petrels, the fifth group making up the family *Procellariidae* are a most interesting

group of between 18 and 22 species, depending upon the authority consulted. Only two breed in British waters, namely Leach's storm petrel and the storm petrel, the latter having several breeding stations in Britain, including St Kilda, where I have spent many happy hours watching their delicate butterfly-like flight over the waves, the tell-tale white rump giving them the appearance of a sea-going house martin. Despite the fact that the tiny birds are vulnerable to predators they are tougher than they look and several species, including the British storm petrel and Wilson's petrel, are trans-equatorial migrants. All the procellariiformes lay but one egg, but once the young have reached the flying stage ringing returns have shown that they can live upwards of 25 years and that a pair may remain bonded for a long period and are also usually faithful to a particular nest site or burrow.

Leach's storm petrel has few nesting sites in Europe although it is widely distributed around the North Pacific and North Atlantic islands. There are, however, significant breeding groups in Iceland, the Faeroes, the Flannan Islands and Sula Sgeir off the west coast of Scotland. The observant British ornithologist is most likely to see *Oceanodroma leucorrhoa* during or immediately following a period of prolonged rough weather when numbers of the lightweight birds are driven ashore, often in considerable numbers. There was a famous 'wreck' in 1957 when over 6,000 individuals were stranded along the coasts of Great Britain and Ireland, with a smaller number of individuals being driven as far as France and even Switzerland.

Finally in this review of the *Procellariidae* we need to consider the four species of diving petrels – a closely knit little group but out on their own little evolutionary limb and restricted to the southern hemisphere. They have short bodies, necks and wings, superficially resembling the little auk of the northern hemisphere. This is an example of what is known as convergent evolution and it really does show how the environment can exert a profound effect on the development of a species. Once more the bird and its environment are intimately linked.

The Pelecaniformes

This order includes five families which may be classed as seabirds, including about thirty species of cormorant, five frigates, three tropics, nine gannets, and the brown pelican (see Table 5). It should be mentioned in passing that the order is completed by the freshwater darters (the *Anhingidae*), of which there are only two species.

Cormorants

Again the various experts differ but most accept that there are some thirty species of cormorant, the family being the most diverse found in the order. They are mainly lovers of tropical and temperate climes but representatives are found in the cooler seas despite apparently having a plumage which is not completely waterproof. This must be a great disadvantage to a bird catching its food by diving and in Britain cormorants and shags standing with their wings held out in an heraldic posture are a common sight. This is obviously their method of drying out their plumage although some have seriously suggested that this position is an effort to assist in pushing down large fish which might otherwise stick in the gullet. To the 'non-naturalists' the cormorants are very much a Jekyll and Hyde family. The Guanay cormorant, nesting on islands off the coast of Peru and Chile, can arguably be described as the most valuable bird in the world. For thousands of years their droppings (guano) accumulated in the largely rain-free climate until in the early nineteenth century it was recognised as a most valuable nitrogenous fertiliser. Between 1848 and 1875 over 20 million tons of the stuff, worth a then staggering sum of £715,000, was shovelled onto trading vessels bound for Europe and North America. Initially there was little concern for the birds and for a time the race for quick profits almost literally destroyed 'the goose which laid the golden egg'. In recent years there has been a successful attempt to farm the crop by providing an area free from predators where the cormorants can nest and defecate in peace.

On the other side of the coin the family's

Cormorant – with white breeding patch on thighs.

efficient method of catching large fish has long been the envy of fishermen and in the Far East the birds were kept and fitted with a metal neck-collar with line attached. This allowed the birds to be released from a boat and to dive for fish. The metal ring prevented the prey being swallowed and the fisherman then simply reeled in his bird before repeating the process. The two British members of the family – the cormorant, often called the great cormorant, and the shag – avoid direct competition by having slightly different habitat preferences. The cormorant is more at ease in shallow waters covering a sandy bottom whilst the shag prefers the deeper waters off a rocky coast. Cormorants have, however, recently taken to exploiting inland waters stocked with trout. It comes as a surprise to many to discover that the British breeding population of shags is around 31,000 pairs and this far outnumbers that of the cormorant, of which only some 8,000 pairs occur. Both species earn the wrath (and the envy) of fishermen, and are often blamed for reducing fish stocks. The ornithologist will,

and should, always argue that overfishing by man as demand outstrips supply is far more devastating to the fish than a few natural predators which in any case are bound to catch the weakest individuals, thus in the end having a beneficial effect on the prey species. There is, however, an even more compelling reason why seabird populations such as these should be left alone and carefully censused. The shag and the cormorant are living in an environment and selecting from it fish which also make up part of the human diet. Should the bird populations remain healthy, we can assume that they are not being poisoned by pollutants in their food. On the other hand, should avian populations decline then the human population might also be at risk. If for no other reason than as an accurate indicator of pollution our seabirds should be studied very carefully – as indeed should many birds in terrestrial and freshwater habitats.

The shag now serves as an indicator species, warning us of contaminated fish.

TABLE 6

Populations of ten gannet colonies in Britain*

Site	Approximate population (number of pairs)
St Kilda	60,000
Grassholme	20,000
Ailsa Craig	16,000
Bass Rock	14,000
Sula Sgeir (Outer Hebrides)	9,000
Stack Skerry (Outer Hebrides)	4,000
Scar Rocks, Wigtown	482
Bempton	200
Fair Isle	50
Flannan Islands (Outer Hebrides)	20

*Note: all colonies listed are increasing.

Frigates

The five species of frigates also find that their inefficient waterproofing and small feet with reduced webbing do not allow them to spend much time actually in contact with the sea, but their large wings and light streamlined bodies are perfectly adapted for cruising the oceans with the minimum expenditure of energy. Their piratical method of obtaining food also reflects their control of the air space over the sea. They chase less efficient aerobats until these are forced to disgorge their last meal, and on other occasions frigates sweep low over the sea snatching small birds from the surface or flying fish from just above it. During the breeding season a swift and deadly flight over a congested colony can be rewarded by a high-protein meal of egg and chicks.

Tropic birds

The three species of tropic birds are also highly efficient flying machines and like the swallows and swifts they have sacrificed a great deal of efficiency of movement on land.

This determines their choice of nest site, which must be in an elevated flat position to allow ease of landing and take-off. Superficially, the tropic birds are more like gulls than pelecaniformes, and downy young hatch from the egg rather than the rather ugly reptilian-looking beast which first greets the parent cormorants. Their flight pattern and calls also tend to be rather gull-like, but their clumsy gait and lack of balance on terra firma are quite typical of their order, as are many details of their internal anatomy.

Gannets and boobies

The gannets and boobies, of which there are nine species, are found all around all continental coasts except Antarctica. The pelecaniformes, unlike the other orders with seabirds amongst their members, have failed to take advantage of the plankton of the sea, but have developed into strikingly efficient aerial divers in pursuit of fish. There are six species of booby, three being widespread throughout the tropics whilst the other three have a much more restricted distribution – especially Abbot's booby, which breeds only on Christmas Island in the Indian Ocean. This species tends to be a solitary nester but as a rule the booby colonies are of incredible size

Gannet and juvenile – Britain is the main breeding area for gannets.

and density. The red-footed booby has a colony of some 150,000 birds sited on Tower Island in the Galapagos, whilst even this vast assemblage is dwarfed by the 350,000 pairs of the Peruvian booby. By comparison the three species of gannet have only relatively small colonies but over 50,000 pairs breed on the St Kilda group and there are smaller groupings on Britain's offshore islands of Bass, Ailsa Craig and Grassholm, which can be very impressive indeed (see Table 6). Atlantic gannets are beautifully streamlined for diving in pursuit of fish, and the vertebrae of the neck and the bone structure of the cranium have become specially strengthened and supported to cope with the stresses imposed by this feeding method. An even more delicate evolutionary development has been a change in the position of the external openings of the nostrils to prevent water being driven up the nose at the instant of splash-down.

Gannets lay only one egg, which is incubated for 42–52 days by the apparently inefficient method of balancing it upon the webs of the feet; this is, however, the warmest area of the body in the absence of a brood patch. For a diving bird such as *Sula bassana* the removal of body feathers at a time when the parent bird has to find enough food for itself and also for a rapidly growing chick as well would make little sense, and sense is one commodity of which nature has a good supply. The amount of food required by the young bird is quite astounding: in just over ten weeks it increases its hatching weight of around 50 grams to over 4,500 grams (there are about 26 grams in 1 ounce). No wonder people with big appetites are called gannets!

The Charadriiformes

Finally in this résumé we come to the members of the large order the charadriiformes, which not only includes the waders (see Chapter 3) but also five families which may be

Great skua regurgitating food to its chick.

called seabirds. These are the skimmers, skuas, gulls, terns and auks.

Skimmers

By far the most bizarre of the seabirds are the three species of skimmers, whose bills have a unique but highly functional adaptation fitting them perfectly for their chosen environment. The lower mandible of the bill grows considerably longer than the upper and the skimmer flies low over the water and literally skims the plankton and fish from on and just below the water surface. The young do not have this mandible differentiation but it develops rapidly as the flying stage approaches – a phenomenon which we have also noted in crossbills and curlews. This self-sufficiency is in stark contrast with the method employed by the piratical skuas, of which there are six species, three being restricted to the northern hemisphere whilst the great skua also occurs in the southern. All are great opportunists with regard to their

feeding and raid seabird colonies and take young and eggs plus the occasional unwary or sickly adult, whilst they will chase and harry in flight any adult until it disgorges its last meal.

Gulls

Few bird families are more cosmopolitan and successful than the gulls, of which there are 44 recognised species. They occupy a wide variety of habitats and perhaps the word sea-gull is less than accurate in some cases. The black-headed gull and the common gull, for example, are often as much birds of inland areas as they are seabirds. The ivory gull, however, finds much of its food as a scavenger among the remains of the meals of polar bears on the ice-packs of the high Arctic. The delightful little kittiwake is also very much a sea-gull. No species, in any bird family, has proved more adaptable than the rapidly increasing herring gull, which has increased fourfold in some areas of Europe since 1925 – a trend which is continuing at the rate of 13% per annum over the country as a whole. The reason for this is not too far to seek, since the

Lesser black-backed — many lesser black-backed gulls which breed in Britain winter in southern Europe.

A great black-backed gull, a voracious predator, stealing eggs from a cliff-top nest.

Common gull at nest.

Common gull chick 'playing possum'.

Black-headed gull preparing to incubate among marram grass.

The herring gull is one of the most common and most aggressive birds in Britain.

Arctic tern – sees more hours of daylight than any other bird.

herring gull has taken full advantage of the modern environment which is so rich in fish docks (despite a recent decline), and sewage outfalls, which raise the nitrogen levels in the sea and increase the plankton which fish feed upon. Add to this the huge mountains of waste food disposed of on the rubbish dumps of our throw-away society and we have the perfect environment for an adaptable scrounger. Something drastic may well have to be done in an effort to combat the herring gull's relentless advance across Europe. They are known to spread disease and there is an obvious danger when concentrations build up around airfields or close to busy flight lanes. High populations of these combined egg-stealers and mobile slaughterhouses for the disposal of chicks can also have devastating effects upon other less harmful species, and this is another compelling reason to view herring gulls with disquiet. They have often had an adverse effect on British tern colonies.

Terns

Worldwide there are 39 species of tern, and although they are widely distributed their main stronghold is the Pacific. But several species venture high into the northern hemisphere to breed – often in large colonies which are easily disturbed, especially in the early stages prior to egg laying. As Europe's coastal sand-dunes, shingle beaches and offshore islands come under ever-increasing pressure from human leisure activities it becomes more and more essential to set up sanctuaries which are closed – even to ornithologists. In Britain we have breeding common terns (about 18,000 pairs), arctic terns (about 45,000 pairs), sandwich terns (about 15,000 pairs), roseate terns (about 1,200 pairs, but declining) and little terns (about 1,600 and declining) (see Table 4). Clearly the last two species are at a dangerously low ebb and need a great deal more protection than they are being given at the moment. The arctic, by far Britain's most common tern, is one of the world's greatest migrants, nesting in high northern latitudes only to have the sense to flee the northern winter to take advantage of the Antarctic summer; thus the crafty bird never sees a winter and enjoys more hours of sunlight than any other creature.

Auks

The final seabird group to be considered here are the auks. Most authorities recognise 22

Puffins (**top**), razorbills (**left**) and guillemots
(**bottom right**).

species. The northern equivalent of the penguins, auks, which have retained the power of flight, have proved equal to every environmental problem thrown at them, but some species have problems coping with oil spills. Nowhere is their adaptability better exemplified than in their choice of nest site, the only areas not acceptable to any species being exposed areas of flat ground. One species, the marbled murrelet, even breeds in hollow trees, sometimes sited some distance inland, whilst others such as the common guillemot choose to nest in large colonies packed along exposed cliff-ledges, and the related razorbills prefer to hide their nests away in crevices, which are obviously less exposed. Puffins also congregate in huge breeding colonies but they choose to nest in burrows which they either excavate themselves or take over from existing tenants, such

A busy puffin colony.

Some authorities think the bill-patterning of razorbills may be unique to the individual bird. This pair certainly have distinct patterning.

A pair of off-duty guillemots.

as rabbits. The fact that puffins' eggs are laid in burrows means that they do not need to be coated with camouflaging pigment, and they are therefore white, but the occasional pigmented egg is found, suggesting that puffins probably nested out in the open many thousands of years ago. Not all auks prefer huge colonies, the razorbill being one example, whilst the black guillemot conceals its egg at the end of a crack in the rock face. Here is the ecological niche theory working in the selection of nest site as well as in feeding techniques. Auks have also suffered at the hand of man – none more than the flightless and therefore vulnerable great auk or garefowl, hunted to extinction for food and for sport. The whole family is now facing a growing threat as man seeks out more and more oil from areas becoming more and more difficult to tap. A report published by the National Environmental Research Council on the Irish seabird wreck of 1969 pointed out that deaths from oil were likely to occur at any time, but that the effects would be more severe at the time of moult or in rough weather, when the birds' natural resources were already stretched to the limit. Before considering these man-created pressures we will turn our attention to a consideration of

how seabirds cope with the problems posed by their natural environment.

The biological problems faced by seabirds

'Water, water everywhere
And all the boards did shrink.
Water, water everywhere
Nor any drop to drink.'

(Coleridge, 'The Ancient Mariner')

Whenever the above poem is read our sympathy goes to the thirsty old sailor and we feel sorry that he can't drink sea water. The 'evil' albatross, in contrast, has the full run of the ocean and has no such problem. The old and in many ways quite logical idea was that seabirds did not drink at all, but obtained liquid from their food. We now know for sure that they actually do drink brine and have an efficient method of desalination. The obvious site of such a mechanism would seem to be the kidney, but it was not difficult to prove that a seabird could only produce urine of about 50% of the salinity of sea water. Logically, then, to desalinate using the kidney the bird would have to produce twice as much urine as the total liquid intake – clearly impossible – and the kidney cannot therefore be the mechanism involved. Work done, principally by Schmidt-Nielson, has shown that excess salt is excreted via a pair of nasal or salt glands sited close to the orbit of the eye. There is plenty of evidence to support the presence of salt glands in other avian families, especially the marine wildfowl and some of the waders, but the best developed are found in the seabirds and these are without doubt one of the most important factors allowing them to range almost where they will over the wide expanses of the world's oceans. Sea water is drunk, the excess salt is removed by the glands, and very strong brine leaves the body via the nostrils. Apart from drinking, feeding at sea must also be important and the seabirds have devised methods of tapping energy supplies from the air, from the surface of the sea, and also from below it.

Some species, such as the frigate birds which harry and bully their prey, feed exclusively on the wing; others, such as the gannets, boobies and pelicans, plunge-dive; terns hover and dive from lower altitudes; and other species swim about on the surface of the water, picking up food directly from it. Many shearwaters and petrels follow this method but they can also submerge occasionally in pursuit of prey, whilst the auks and penguins dive deep beneath the waves. These two families thus have a similar feeding niche, but never come into direct competition because they occur in opposite hemispheres. In some cases, especially in the shearwaters, the feeding niche is shared by having a day shift and a night shift. There is a regular rise and fall of the various planktonic organisms over a 24-hour period, some being on the surface at night others during the daylight hours. Birds such as the Manx shearwater often take advantage of a night feed and in some cases the prey may even produce its own bioluminescence and so be clearly visible in the dark. Specialised feeding, often miles offshore, often leads to problems during the raising of the young. This is particularly acute in many of the procellariiformes. The solution usually lies in the provision of meals of huge proportions at irregular intervals, and the Manx shearwater is a good illustration of this.

However successful seabirds have been in breaking the physical ties with the land, no species has come anywhere near to being able to breed at sea. The terrestrial site in which the egg or eggs are laid is vital to all. In the actual selection of the site the theory of the ecological niche is again clearly demonstrated. The cormorant and the shag occur around the coasts of Britain and where the two are found in the same area the cormorant is able to tolerate a more exposed area for the construction of its nest than the shag, which seems to have an aversion to being splashed while incubating. Among the gulls, the kittiwake prefers narrow ledges in contrast to the herring gull's preference for wider areas of rock or sand-dunes. Species such as the black-headed gull often avoid competition by selecting an inland nesting niche. I have already discussed the variation in the nesting sites of the auks. There are more subtle, but nevertheless detectable, differences in the nesting sites chosen by the five British species of terns, on areas of exposed shingle, sand-dunes or grassy islands.

Even this brief discussion of the feeding and breeding niches of seabirds will show that it is in these two vulnerable areas that human activity can often have a devastating effect. Pollution of the oceans by hydrocarbon-based pesticides, herbicides and fungicides can, sometimes very subtly indeed, enter the food chains and oil can clog and affect the waterproofing of the feathers of diving birds, especially auks. Radiation, both natural and man-generated can also have an effect whilst too many people in the wrong place (from the birds' point of view) at the wrong time can also be literally lethal. The remainder of this chapter is therefore devoted to a consideration of these factors.

Opposite

A colony of kittiwakes on the Farne Islands.

The effect of human activities on seabirds

Birds have been subjected to hunting pressure since the human species first evolved, but in the early days of our history only the breeding colonies were really vulnerable and the seas and oceans were havens for the birds. Things have changed, since human enterprises now reach out into and even far beneath the seas. Many of the fish on the continental shelf are declining drastically and show signs of going the way of the whales. Some species such as gulls and the fulmar may well have benefited from these activities, as we have already seen, but others which are catchers of fish in their own right – such as terns, cormorants and auks – may have suffered in competition with fishermen. In 1972 Tull and his fellow workers pointed out that salmon nets in Greenland enmeshed and drowned upwards of 500,000 Brunnich's guillemots (also called thick-billed murres) each year. In Britain puffins, shags, gannets and common guillemots are also frequently caught up in fishing nets. Those who study and comment upon bird populations should, however, take great care to ensure that they do not blame every declining population on human activities because changing climatic conditions also play their part.

The main problem of the 1980s must be pollution and this has been the case since the 1950s, when a group of organo-chloride insecticides were developed – the most deadly in the family being eldrin, aldrin and dieldrin. These were effective in killing insects, but it soon became obvious that birds in agricultural areas were suffering. These poisons are so long-lasting that they can be flushed by rain into the rivers and thence to the coastal seas and may even be carried thousands of miles on ocean currents. The organo-chlorides, although not very soluble in water, are very soluble in fat and can remain in living tissue for periods of more than ten years. Sophisticated techniques for identifying the poisons led to their discovery in many bird species, including sandwich terns, guillemots, puffins, shags, great skuas and kittiwakes, and even in the tissues of penguins in Antarctica.

The poisons accumulate in the fat deposits of the animals at the top of the food chains, such as birds and mammals, including man. As long as these deposits are not drawn upon all is well, but when the creature is under pressure and needs to use its reserves the poisons are released into the bloodstream and may well deliver the death blow. Such an occurrence may account for the sudden appearance of large numbers of dead seabirds on our beaches, such as the well documented Irish Sea disaster of 1969 and on the Mersey estuary ten years later. In the 1969 disaster the bodies of over 17,000 birds were found, although as many as three times this figure must have perished. Hodgate reported on the situation in 1971 and although he did not reach any firm conclusions he did point out that many birds showed signs of starvation, possibly due to the potentially lethal combination of moulting, disease and strong gales. It was mentioned in passing that the condition of the birds may have been aggravated by organic poisons and certain heavy metals, including mercury, copper, arsenic and lead. Lead was certainly implicated in the 1979 seabird mortality on the Mersey. It was suggested that much of the lead causing the problem may have been accumulating in the sediments for years and the same may be said for the long-lasting organo-chloride pesticides and the heavy metals which have been used in the paint industry since the 1930s. The problem is therefore not over once restrictions have been imposed, for it may take many years for the poisons to work through the system. The oceans are the sink of the world. They will be the last to feel the effects of banned pollutants and they will be the last to be rid of them.

Such pollutants are invisible killers, in complete contrast with the effects of pollution by oil, which rightly or wrongly receives the major blast of criticism when the inter-relationship between birds and the marine environment is discussed. There have been natural oil leakages ever since the oil deposits were formed from the pressed bodies of small animals in the shallow seas of the Carboniferous Period. The modern problem is not that oil spills occur, but rather where they occur. The first headline event was as long ago as 1907 when 2 million gallons of crude oil spewed out of a stricken schooner off the Scillies. Since then the traffic in oil has escalated and spillage by accident – and, sad to say, occasionally by design when tanks are flushed out at sea – presents a continual threat to seabird populations. As the tapping of North Sea oil gathers momentum the big danger is a massive oil spill close to the seabird cities. Oil companies have done much to increase safety and to prevent illegal tank flushing, but there are still many unscrupulous owners and skippers sailing under flags of convenience who flout the law and could not care less about wildlife or the environment providing they meet the delivery dates which ensure fat profit margins.

The most immediate effects of oil pollution on seabirds are seen around estuaries and here the work of Schachter and Serwer published in 1971 is of great interest. They showed that twice as much oil reaches the sea via rivers from land-based activities than from spillage from tankers and oil installations such as rigs and pipelines. Obviously the best answer is to physically prevent birds ever coming into contact with oil but as this is clearly a utopian wish other solutions must be sought. Once birds are oiled they cannot fly nor can they dive for food, and they are therefore washed ashore, often in a pathetic state. Methods of cleaning seabirds have improved greatly in recent years as a result of research carried out at such places as the University of Newcastle upon Tyne and at the RSPCA's oiled seabird unit based at Little Creech in Somerset. It can take up to two hours to clean a common guillemot and as long as six hours to deal with a stressed and reluctant gannet. The whole process requires great care if the bird is to be released with both cleaned and water-repellent plumage. Once the process is complete the birds are kept in holding rooms overnight before being released into ponds to test the success of the treatment. Eventually they are released, but there can be no doubt that many birds – especially razorbills, guillemots and

puffins – still die despite all efforts. There are success stories. It was reported in the *Marine Pollution Bulletin* published in 1980 that a guillemot treated at Little Creech and released at Portland, Dorset, on December 22nd, 1977, was recovered on April 5th, 1980, at Crosshaven, Eire, again oiled, this time fatally. Its life had at least been considerably extended. However much we, as individuals, may wish to keep an oiled bird it does urgently need skilled treatment, and this can be obtained by ringing the local branch of the RSPCA, which will be listed in the yellow pages. In the case of a large number of birds being found oiled then contact with the RSPCA headquarters at Horsham (telephone 0403–64181) is recommended.

If we are aware of the problems faced by seabirds something can be done to help them survive in an environment which is tough enough already without us adding to the problem. It is becoming increasingly necessary to provide sanctuaries where vulnerable species can breed insulated from the pressures imposed by our increasing leisure, for which we need caravans, holiday camps and 'quiet' beaches. All that the birds need is a fair share of the quiet beach – especially species such as the roseate and little terns, which are declining due to a combination of loss of habitat, either physically or as a result of disturbance. Once local authorities are made aware of the responsibility they have when rare birds are found on land under their control they should be encouraged to maintain the area as a sanctuary. It is unfair to expect ratepayers to foot the bill: costs could be met by government grant or better still an arrangement with a naturalist trust or bird society with a willing army of unpaid workers. This will work providing disturbance of birds at crucial phases in the breeding cycle is fiercely resisted.

Thus the bird *and* its environment should be uppermost in our minds as we seek to preserve our own natural heritage. The bird's problem today may well be ours tomorrow.

5 Rivers

Surviving in and around a river is by no means as easy as in many other habitats. There are problems associated with staying in position when faced with a one-way flow of water and the great variations in both volume and velocity during times of heavy rain on the upland catchment areas. These variations are obviously at their most extreme in the highland areas and are attenuated as the watercourse widens, levels out, and finally meets the sea. Whilst it is possible to divide rivers both physically and biologically into zones along their lengths it should be stressed that no two rivers can ever be identical and the effect of human activities are more marked in some rivers than in others. The rivers of south-eastern Britain are also substantially different in character from those of the north and west, the southern waters rising from low hills or even oozing out of wells not much above sea level, whilst those in northern parts spring from the summits and slopes of the highlands and descend as heaving, dancing torrents of froth. A few birds – such as the resident grey wagtail and the dipper as well as the common sandpiper, a summer visitor – are able to handle these extreme conditions, each tackling the problem in its own unique way and exploiting its own ecological niche.

Grey wagtail *Motacilla cinerea*
Between 25,000 and 50,000 pairs of this perky 18 centimetre (about 7 inches) long species really seem to enjoy turbulent streams with rocky beds. Even in winter these stretches of fast-moving water are less likely to freeze than the slower stretches and there are plenty of insect larvae skulking under the stones. A large number of the flying insects which so grace a riverside in summer have aquatic larvae: the larvae of stoneflies, mayflies and dragonflies all figure in the diet of the grey wagtail. The species is easily recognised by the yellow on the breast and beneath the tail

coverts whilst the back is slate-grey, which accounts for the vernacular name and distinguishes this bird from the even more colourful summer-visiting yellow wagtail (*Motacilla flava*), which does not, however, favour such a tough habitat. When viewed from a distance the very long tail of the grey wagtail can be seen for what it is – an aid to balance as the bird hops delicately from pebble to pebble amongst a roaring and potentially dangerous torrent. The tail is also used during display when the male spreads the caudal feathers, and another exciting feature is the

Yellow wagtail (**top**) and grey wagtail (**bottom**).

chasing flights during which the characteristic 'tzissic-tzissic' is clearly heard. In breeding plumage the male's black throat-patch is clearly seen and enables him to be distinguished from his mate who lacks this feature. The pair are not too particular regarding the choice of nest site and may take over the old nest of a dipper, whilst a hole in bank or under tree roots may prove to be acceptable. The female does all the building but the male is seldom far from her side and often gives her protection whilst she feeds in peace and can therefore more easily develop the eggs within her. The clutch is usually of between four and six eggs and they are incubated for about a fortnight by both sexes. The fact that both parents work hard to feed the young enables them to fly in about 13 days and enables a second brood to be raised providing the first eggs have been laid before the end of April. On the whole the grey wagtail is resident and pairs tend to be in territory by January, moving towards the coast only in the most severe weather.

Dipper *Cinclus cinclus*

Dippers show a similar behaviour pattern but, instead of feeding on the edge of the river, dippers employ a bold and apparently fearless method of walking into the main stream.

Dippers are about 18 centimetres (7 inches) in length and some 30,000 pairs breed in Britain. There is nothing the species likes more than a tumbling stream and roaring waterfall unless it be a babbling brook spanned by a bridge. Both these attractive habitats provide adequate food and suitable nesting sites. The white-bibbed chubby little bird with the short wren-like tail and chestnut belly bobs up and down on a stone like a

The dipper – a common resident along mountain streams.

confident ballet star before charging headlong into the foaming brook. Once submerged it holds its wings at an angle to the current so that the force of water holds it down. A quick search under stones reveals choice items of food such as aquatic insects, crustaceans, molluscs and small fishes. The wings are then 'folded up' and the dipper bobs to the surface like a cork. Once safe on a rock the bird blinks its opaque third eyelid (possessed by all birds and called the nictitating membrane) and this squeezes the excess water from the eye. The chubby little body is no doubt rich enough in fat and the feathers sufficiently water-repellent for the dipper to take frequent dips even in the depths of winter – indeed, breeding commences very early in the year, nest construction often being well advanced by the end of February. It is a domed structure made of moss and lined with leaves, a necessary protection when close to waterfalls and rivers in spate. It is usually stated that both sexes build the nest, but my work on the species suggests there is some division of labour and in the magazine *British Birds* in August 1980 I published a short report on this subject:

'On 31st March 1978 at Hardcastle Craggs, Hebden Bridge, Yorkshire, I found the nest of a pair of dippers *Cinclus cinclus* under an overhang about 3 metres above a swiftly-flowing stream; it was about 70% completed. For over an hour, in very good light, I watched the two birds building. During this time, ten bundles of grass were collected from the edge of the stream and incorporated into the nest; and five beech *Fagus sylvatica* leaves were retrieved from the stream, making a total of 15 deliveries to the nest. This fits the nest-building description given by Bruce Campbell and James Ferguson-Lees [see bibliography]; on this occasion, however, one dipper did all the collecting and flew to a flat stone in the centre of the stream, while the other flew down to join its mate where the material was passed from the first's bill to the second's. The builder then returned to the nest and the collector continued searching for new material.'

The sexes are impossible to distinguish in the dipper and I wonder just how isolated the incident described above really is. There is, however, no doubt that the female alone incubates the clutch of from three to six eggs for 16 days, after which both parents feed the young, which are able to fly within 25 days, and this gives ample time for a second brood to be attempted. A special feature of dipper behaviour is the fact that the territory is linear and both ends need to be defended against intrusion by rivals. For this reason both sexes can produce the rather sweet warbling song which so delights the upland naturalist.

Common sandpiper *Tringa hypoleucos*

In the spring upland naturalists may also be treated to a display of aquabatics and aerobatics by a sample of the 50,000 pairs of common sandpipers which arrive from Africa from middle to late April.

Common sandpipers have usually completed the building cycle by late September and departed for warmer climes, but there is an increasing tendency for a few birds to overwinter in Britain. It is in late April or early May, however, that these 20 centimetre (8 inch), long-legged, thin, straight-billed, white-rumped waders with the characteristic flight return to grace our rivers. As the males chase the females low over the water during courtship, the flight pattern, during which the wings are held at the end of the downstroke in a typical bowed position, distinguishes the common sandpiper from every other European wader. The 'twee-wee-wee' call is uttered in flight and also from any convenient song post. The typical bobbing movement is somewhat reminiscent of the dipper, and some workers have suggested that the movement gives both species camouflage against the background of flowing water. The food consists of crustaceans, insect larvae, worms and molluscs, and vegetation forms a small but significant and possibly important proportion of the diet. Sandpipers scour the riverside and do not submerge in pursuit of prey, so there is no direct competition either with the dipper or with the smaller grey wagtail.

The riverside is also the favoured nesting site although the areas surrounding water-

falls tend to be avoided in favour of shingle areas or areas of vegetation overhanging the river. These areas are usually safe, but are occasionally vulnerable in times of sudden thunderstorms and subsequent flash floods. The usual clutch is four eggs laid in a grass-lined scrape and both sexes share the 3½-week incubation period, after which they look after but do not physically feed the young. Only one brood is produced and long before they can fly the young begin to walk downstream with their parents and quite significant flocks begin to gather on the estuaries prior to the return migration. This means that, although the upper reaches of the river are preferred for breeding, common sandpipers are quite likely to be found strolling along almost any bank of any river during the late summer.

The upland streams, often tributaries of larger rivers, may also provide a suitable habitat for the ring ouzel which breeds among the bracken, heather and bilberry of the wet moorland catchment areas and for the goosander, which is becoming increasingly

Common sandpipers arrive in April to breed in Britain.

common as a breeding species in upland Britain.

Goosander *Mergus merganser*
Goosanders show a distinct preference for substantial rivers which slice through upland plantations and finds little to please it in the smaller streams which tumble down open hillsides. The food of this, the largest of the sawbilled ducks, consists mainly of fish, which are captured by diving in the deeper pools of the river. The serrated edges of the goosander's bill slope backwards and enable the prey to be gripped firmly. Its favourite nest site is in a hollow tree or amongst holes in a heathery or shrub-lined bank. Any number of eggs from seven to sixteen may be laid in a down-lined nest and incubated for about 5 weeks by the patient and wary duck, the drake playing no role in the event. Within two or three days of hatching the ducklings are persuaded to scramble or even jump out of

The goosander — a saw-billed duck.

the nest and follow their mother to the river. I was once fortunate enough to witness a group of eleven young goosanders leap, apparently without fear, from a nest hole in a Scots pine and fall to the earth some twenty metres (sixty feet) below, their light bodies suffering no damage. A quick shake was followed by a scuttling run towards the duck who was calling for her brood to get a move on. The first recorded breeding of the goosander in Britain took place in Perthshire in 1871, but its range has now spread to northern England, perhaps helped by tree planting and a reduction in persecution. Wetter, cooler summers are also likely to have been a major factor. In any event the breeding population is now over 1,000 pairs, a dramatic and exciting increase by any standards. The male at 65 centimetres (26 inches) is larger than his mate and sexual dimorphism is very pronounced. He has a green head, although at a distance this looks black and contrasts sharply with the pinkish-white feathers on the breast and the flanks. The lack of any distinct crest serves to distinguish this species both from the red-breasted merganser and from the female goosander, which has a rich chestnut head and a straggling crest. There is also a clear white patch on her throat, breast and wing. Both sexes have red legs and bill but those of the male are considerably brighter. The juveniles resemble the females, but whatever the age, sex, or season the goosander is a species guaranteed to grace any stretch of water.

The threats on the lower reaches

As the river reaches the lower land its progress is slowed and it meanders gently through fertile fields and busy towns. Birds which evolved in these niches have been particularly hard hit by human industry, especially where the working population is high. Pollution takes many forms, including the discharge of raw sewage into the nearest watercourse. In the early days of the development of villages and towns the discharge of human and animal excrement into rivers enriched the waters and encouraged plant growth on which animal life depended. As described in Chapter 3, too much sewage can deplete oxygen levels to such an extent that animals cannot breathe and the river dies. Likewise the discharge of coloured dyes, china clay or even mud can prevent light penetrating the water, and the river plants and the animal life dependent upon food made by photosynthesis will perish. Many Cornish rivers are permanently prevented from flourishing but in some cases the effect may be temporary and the river may recover surprisingly quickly. In the early days of the construction of the M6 motorway the River Lune was badly affected by the mud and slurry churned up by the massive machines, but now the traffic speeds on its way to and from the Scottish border and the Lune runs clear and healthy.

Not all our rivers have been lucky enough to be inconvenienced so temporarily and some have their banks thickly lined with factories discharging acid, alkalis, oil and heavy metals whilst even steam and hot water can be lethal when oxygen levels are already low. Cold water has more oxygen dissolved in it than hot – this is why a kettle bubbles as it boils, the air being driven out – and a power station or large factory near a sewage outlet can kill all life in that particular stretch of river. Assuming that the middle stretches of the river are relatively unpolluted, then the birds and other wildlife still have problems in competing for space with the ever-demanding human species with more money and time on our hands than ever before. The discarded line from an otherwise inoffensive angler can be lethal to an inquisitive or hungry bird whilst river boat traffic can adversely affect feeding, breeding and roosting. The problems faced by birds from anglers and boaters along with some possible solutions will be considered in the next chapter, but so far as river birds are concerned the middle section, providing pollution levels and disturbances are not too

great, supports several attractive species. The most colourful of all is the kingfisher, but other typical and attractive species include the resident dabchick, which sails around in the slow-moving current, and the summer-visiting sand martins, which hawk for flies over the water and nest in the banks. The riverside alders provide shelter for the heron (described in the next chapter) and food for the mainly winter visitor the siskin, whilst in summer the water meadows are graced by the canary-coloured yellow wagtail. The reed bunting is found all the year round feeding and breeding in the vegetation bordering rivers and in recent times has been adversely affected by the construction of housing estates close to watercourses, which are so attractive to wildlife and property developers.

Kingfisher *Alcedo atthis*
Kingfishers are unlikely to allow the unwary riverside stroller to get a long hard look at them since they are amongst the most alert and wary species on the British list. All that is seen is a blur of wings and a flicker of bright, flashing reflected blue or green light as the kingfisher quickly shifts to a safer perch. The body length is around 17 centimetres (nearly 7 inches) but the dagger-like bill is over 4 centimetres (1½ inches) and looks large and cumbersome, but its power spells disaster to fish of often surprising size which are grabbed following an impressive plunge dive and then carried to a perch where they are clubbed to death by this aptly named king of fishers. The upper parts of the head and back are blue-green and the underparts are orange-coloured whilst the feet are as red as sealing-wax. Most ornithological texts state that the bill is black and that the sexes are alike but some orni-thologists, myself included, are convinced that it is possible to separate male and female kingfishers by the bill colour. In the adult male both the upper and lower mandible are plain black, but the lower mandible of the female's bill is quite obviously red. The total breeding population in Britain is between 5,500 and 9,000 pairs and the distribution is restricted to the lowland reaches of rivers situated in the southern and midland section of the British Isles. There are very few birds in

No small fish is safe from the attention of
kingfishers.

Scotland, where conditions are too tough.
Even in the much milder climate in the
extreme south-west of England bad weather
can decimate the population – as can pollution
and 'river management', which often involves
uprooting trees, straightening out meanders
and raising and strengthening banks, often by
the indiscriminate use of concrete. Plants
which can block drainage schemes are treated
with herbicides which enter the food chains
and the kingfisher at the top of the chain
suffers badly. Recovery, however, can be
quite quick due to the protracted breeding
which begins with the males' 'butterfly'
display flight often as early as February and
can end with the flight of the third brood in
September. Nest building begins when both
sexes hurl themselves at the river bank until a
platform large enough to stand on is produced. They then bore a tunnel up to a metre
(3 feet) in length, ending in a circular chamber
in which from six to eight eggs are laid.
They are incubated by both sexes for about 20
days and about a month later the young fly
after being fed by both sexes. During their
first few days away from the nest, which by

now stinks with rotten fish and excreta, the
young kingfishers are vulnerable to wind and
rain and many die whilst others perish because
they fail to learn the techniques of diving soon
enough. Despite the unsavoury stench of the
nest subsequent broods are usually raised in
the same nest and it is small wonder that adult
kingfishers bathe a lot in order to rid themselves of the stinking green slime which oozes
from the nest hole. A quick dip and a good
preen, however, soon restore the bird to its
elegance.

Dabchick *Tachybaptus ruficollis*
Also aptly named the little grebe, the
dabchick is only 27 centimetres (just over
10½ inches) long and although the sturdy
bird is quite happy in still waters it does seem
quite willing and able to handle the spate
waters thundering through the middle reaches
of rivers. In summer plumage the smallest of
our grebes is dark brown, but with lovely
splashes of chestnut on the front of the neck,
throat and cheeks. It is too early yet to be sure
but my researches suggest that the pattern of
these chestnut patches is unique to a particular
bird and, like human fingerprints, can be used
to identify an individual. Both the base of the
bill and the gape are bright yellow but in

The little grebe, also known as the dabchick, on its nest.

winter the appearance is quite drab by comparison, although its busy, alert behaviour still makes the little grebe a fascinating bird to watch. Although it seems much more inclined to fly than other grebes, the dabchick still prefers to dive and swim away when danger threatens and its food is also obtained by diving. Small fish, crustaceans, aquatic insects and molluscs are important items in the diet, which also includes a small quantity of vegetable matter. There is also some evidence to suggest that feathers are eaten, but this habit is nowhere nearly so common as in the great crested grebe.

The population is adversely affected by tough winters, but more than 10,000 pairs now breed in Britain and, as with the kingfisher, the recovery from these troughs is quick due to two and often three broods being raised during the protracted breeding season, which begins in March and may still be in full swing at the end of August. The preferred nest site is among overhanging branches or mergent vegetation such as yellow flag or rushes. Vegetation is heaped up and the clutch of from four to six eggs is laid in a depression. Both sexes incubate but some extra assistance may be provided by the heat generated as the vegetation decays. Within 24 days the young

are afloat and feeding. If the incubating bird leaves the nest to feed, drink or defecate, and is not flushed in panic, the eggs are carefully covered. The care given to the young depends upon whether or not the female produces a subsequent clutch. If this is the case the male tends the young on his own (and the young from a previous brood also help when three clutches are laid), but if the hen is free she takes her full share of the responsibility. Parent grebes, however, have only to supervise the young, which feed themselves, although they do occasionally give piggy-back rides to the tired or perhaps cold babies.

Sand martin *Riparia riparia*
The young of the sand martin are much more demanding and require regular feeding by their parents. Sand martins are among the first of the summer migrants to arrive and in a reasonable spring there may be young in their nests before May is out. Three broods are often produced before the end of September. Although obviously not affected by our harsh winters, the population of sand martins, once around 250,000 pairs, was sadly reduced by

Sand martin.

recent drought conditions which affected the North African Sahel region, through which the migrating birds passed and halted for refreshment. The same factor also decimated the population of white throats, which follow a similar route. Sand martins are distinguished from the rest of the swallow tribe by their upper plumage of dusty brown, white beneath, the short and only slightly forked tail and prominent brown band across the chest. The slender body is only 12 centimetres (4¾ inches) long, making it the smallest of the swallow family. The species is always gregarious and even meal times consist of aerial flocks snapping up insects alongside river banks.

The nest colonies are often in the sandy banks of streams and rivers, but railway embankments and even sea cliffs are used on occasions. Drainage pipes are also used in dry weather, but this can be a lethal choice during times of flash floods. The eggs, of which there are usually four or five, are white and laid on a mat of straw and feathers at the end of a short tunnel bored by both sexes. This sharing of domestic duties extends to the incubation period of 14 days and during the 20 days it takes for the brood to fledge. Whilst they are with us sand martins look to the riverside to provide all the requirements to sustain life. This contrasts sharply with the demands made by siskins, which tend to rely upon the riverside alder trees to provide their winter foods, whilst in summer the habitat requirements are completely different as they seek out suitable conifer plantations.

Siskin *Carduelis spinus*

Although the British breeding population is now around 20,000 pairs, the colonisation of these islands has been relatively recent. However, siskins have always flooded into our river valleys during the colder months of the year. There has been, and still is for that matter, a tendency to confuse this tiny 12 centimetre (4¾ inch) finch with blue tits, which also feed on alder seeds during the winter. The thing which surprises me is that the species seems unable to find sufficient seed in the larch woods during the winter and has to switch habitats. Being a finch, the powerful seed-eating bill distinguishes the siskin from titmice and sexual dimorphism is sufficiently pronounced to enable the sexes to be separated in the field. The male is basically yellow-green but has black on the chin and on the crown whilst the rump is yellow. There is also a greenish-yellow wing bar and the same colour etches the outside of the tail feathers. The female is considerably darker and more evenly coloured and there is no black on her head. In any event, the presence of siskins along riversides during the dull, dark days of winter can add summer colour and help to spawn thoughts of long hot days, the sound of soaring lark and the droning of bees.

Yellow wagtail *Motacilla flava*

About 25,000 pairs of these wonderfully coloured birds come to us during April from West Africa. Many pairs breed on the water meadows and they are typified by the bounding flight, fast trotting walk and flicking tail. The males are canary yellow, the females being duller, but there is such a great deal of variation in the plumage that several geographical races have been recognised. The most common subspecies found in Britain is the yellow wagtail (*Motacilla flava flavissima*), but we also get the blue-headed variety (*Motacilla flava flava*), the breeding male of this subspecies being typified by a bluish-grey rather than green crown and ear coverts. There is also a white eye stripe and chin in the blue-head whilst in *Motacilla flava flavissima* the stripe is yellow. There is evidence that the two subspecies can interbreed, so the taxonomy of the species is difficult to sort out.

Following enthusiastic and vocal chases plus an undulating trilling song flight by the male, the fertilised hen builds a fur-lined nest amongst the rank vegetation and is responsible for incubating the four to six eggs on her own, a task which takes about a fortnight. Some books suggest that the male occasionally assists in the incubation and my own observations tend to suggest that the cock does slightly less than 10% of the incubation. There is no doubt, however, that the fortnight spent in feeding the young until they can fly is a joint operation, and is so successful that a second clutch is almost always attempted.

Few if any of our habitats have been more threatened than our water meadows since agriculture is more efficient and intensive, leaving areas of lush-looking valleys ripe for the 'cultivation' of executive bungalows overlooking a winding river on which the family boat can be moored. Marginal land – valuable bird habitat – is eagerly drained. Plants of the water meadows disappear and are replaced by rockeries, rose gardens, lawns and neatly stacked compost heaps. River meanders are straightened, ugly ponds drained to make room for brightly coloured paddling pools, and bird song replaced by the drone of lawn mowers and the strident throbbing of Radio One. The yellow wagtail has retreated permanently and until recently the reed bunting was another species which, having evolved on the reedbeds, found it difficult to cope. It is now making a remarkable comeback, having learned to live in gardens and in winter to take food from bird tables.

Reed bunting *Emberiza schoeniclus*

Reed buntings are often overlooked by those beginning the study of birds since they bear a more than superficial resemblance to the ubiquitous house sparrows, which are never even given a second glance. Reed buntings are 15 centimetres (6 inches) long, with the males having a black head and throat with a very prominent white collar. The female has a brown head but the buff-coloured eye stripe and throat distinguishes her from the sparrow, as also do the clearly seen moustachial streak and the white outer portion of the tail

Opposite
Reed buntings have recently started to visit bird tables, although they still nest in reeds.

The snipe uses its remarkably long bill to probe the mud for food in marshy meadows along rivers, undrained farmland and coastal marshes.

feathers. The breeding population still exceeds 500,000 pairs and in winter an influx of continental birds more than doubles this count. As can be realised from a glance at the bill shape, the reed bunting thrives on seeds, which are found in quantity in the low-lying damp and boggy areas around rivers but increasingly these days in gardens, which indicates that a shift in habitat has been successfully accomplished. The 'tweek-tweek-tweek-ti-ti-ti-tick' song of the male seeking a mate can be heard from March onwards, after which the mated female selects a nest site close to the ground in a low bush or tuft of grass. Into the grass-lined nest she lays four or five plain bluish-coloured eggs and incubates them, with just a little help from her mate, in about two weeks. He does, however, help with the feeding and the fledging period can be as short as ten days and

seldom takes longer than thirteen, which gives the pair ample time to rear two or even three broods in a season.

Reed buntings breed along any river which has a generous fringe of vegetation; they even find estuaries and salt-marshes very much to their liking. Eventually rivers reach the sea and, at times when the fresh water freezes over, the salt present in these areas keeps the water open and offers a refuge in which the birds from the upper reaches may find enough food to survive. In the winter of 1962–3, for example, I witnessed a hungry kingfisher hovering just like a kestrel before plunging into the estuary in search of a meal. These estuaries (see Chapter 3) are, on balance, more important to birds in winter than in summer and two species in particular are typical of this habitat. These are the brent goose and the wigeon.

Canada goose (**left**) and Brent goose (**right**).

Brent goose *Branta bernicla*

The brent goose is a compact and easily recognised goose varying in size from 55 to 60 centimetres (22–24 inches). Whilst there are pale areas on the underside the dorsal surface is very dark, which makes the thin white collar just behind the head very noticeable indeed. Once found fairly commonly on the estuaries around the British Isles, the brent has become much scarcer in recent years but there is some sign of an upward swing in the fortunes of the species. In fact there are two subspecies occurring in Britain. The dark-breasted brent goose breeds in Russia and winters in England, the main area being Foulness, which at one time was earmarked to become London's third airport. It was the great cost which stopped the scheme, but not before a competent research team had been set to work to discover as much as possible about the biology of the brent goose which would have caused problems to aircraft coming in to land close to the migration route of hundreds of big heavy birds. It was found that Foulness was at times the home to almost a quarter of a million birds of several species including over 20% of the world population of dark-bellied brent geese. The pale-breasted subspecies breeds in Spitzbergen, Greenland and Arctic Canada and a proportion winter in Ireland. This is the race which occurs in Northumberland.

The diet of all the brents consists mainly of vegetable matter, including farm crops which makes it rather unpopular with farmers and therefore a difficult species to protect. It goes without saying that all threatened species ought to be protected, but even the most fanatical conservationist must have sympathy with farmers who see their profits being eaten and their families' livelihood threatened. Any answer is likely to be something of a compromise but some sort of 'goose rate support grant' may well have to be thought about, or attractive feeding stations set up, as has been done by the Wildfowl Trust at Martin Mere near Southport for the pink-footed geese. Perhaps the best answer is to try hard to conserve natural habitats and food supplies. This would also benefit species which share the estuarine habitat – other geese, swans and ducks, including the delightful wigeon.

Wigeon *Anas penelope*

The wigeon is one of Europe's most familiar ducks from the point of view of both sight and sound. The male has a chestnut head with a yellowish patch on the forehead which can be seen from a considerable distance even in poor visibility. The 'whee-oo' whistle has a haunting quality well known to those who enjoy bird watching on the saltings or in more recent years at inland wetland sites. The male also has a striking patch of white on the wing, clearly seen during flight. The female is much duller and mainly brownish but the bluish bill can be seen when she is still and the pointed tail and white belly are typical of both sexes and can be clearly seen in flight. The body length is about 45–55 centimetres (18–22 inches).

The wigeon is mainly a wintering species with only about 500 pairs breeding, mainly in upland areas and still largely confined to Scotland, following the first pair to nest in Sutherland in 1834. Where breeding does occur there does seem a tendency towards the development of small colonies. Each nest is concealed among vegetation and lined with grass and down. The female alone incubates the seven to nine cream-coloured eggs for just over three weeks. As soon as the female arrives at the nearest suitable water she is likely to be joined by her mate. The wigeon differs in this from many other species of duck.

The upland breeding habitat may be shared by the teal (*Anas crecca*), of which as many as 6,000 pairs may breed in Britain. Whilst these populations are so low there is unlikely to be competition between the two species for breeding sites and as the diet is different – teal dabbling in shallow waters, wigeon pulling up grasses on land – the two species can live together in peace and harmony.

Eel-grass

There is potentially some competition between the wigeon and the brent goose since both have long been partial to a meal of eel-grass. There are three species of eel-grass, which are the only flowering plants able to grow and flower completely submerged in the sea. At high tide they look like patches of

Pochard (**left**) and wigeon (**right**).

green seaweed. Seaweeds do not have roots and a quick investigation at the base of the stem will reveal the evidence that the plant is in fact eel-grass. During the 1930s eel-grass declined in both Europe and North America, possibly due to a virus disease. The wigeon and the brent geese which were so dependent upon it reacted to its loss in very different ways. The brents remained close to the coast and their population may well have declined due to the failure to find a reliable alternative source of food. It would seem that they were just beginning to solve the problem by switching to farm crops when the eel-grass began to recover. This recovery may well be the answer to the farmer's prayer. The wigeon, on the other hand, proved more adaptable, and moved inland to find rich pickings from the grass around reservoirs, lakes, and what marshes still remain in Britain.

Whilst human activities have often adversely affected wildlife, there have also been significant, and too often understated, advantages. The construction of reservoirs, the flooding of gravel pits and old mine workings, and the abandonment of canals have been of great benefit to several species and it is such beneficiaries which are the subject of the next chapter.

Opposite
The osprey – an expert plunge-diver and fisher.

6 Still Waters

A Scots loch, an English or Welsh lake, a mountain tarn, a man-made reservoir, a farmer's pond, an engineer's canal, a miner's flooded subsidence, a gravel or clay extractor's pit, all these fall within the scope of this chapter. There are also large expanses of wetland and marsh, of which the Norfolk Broads is the most obvious but areas such as the Somerset levels, the Cambridgeshire Fens and Leighton Moss in Cumbria also spring to mind. To define all these areas under one heading is clearly impossible but a study of the bird life can be of some assistance because, although there is some overlapping, each area

seems to be preferred by at least one species either as a feeding or a breeding niche and sometimes the habitat fulfils both demands.

The upland lochs of Scotland

Many of these lovely expanses of water, such as Lomond, are very similar to the English and Welsh lakes, others are sea lochs, but some upland lochs, often surrounded by damp, swirling mist, are the home, for at least part of the year, for two of Britain's most unusual

and attractive birds. These are the osprey and the sharply contrasting red-throated diver.

Osprey *Pandion haliaetus*

The osprey is a good example of a bird which makes use of two very different habitats. It chooses the fringes of a pine forest for breeding and the lochs of upland Scotland and sometimes one of its magnificent rivers for fishing. It also exemplifies the theory of the ecological niche by tapping a food supply not regularly used by other birds of prey in the area. There are two famous sites in Britain where ospreys can be watched under carefully wardened, but to the birds perfectly natural, conditions. These are at Loch Garten and the Loch of the Lowes, the former being controlled by the RSPB, the latter by the Scottish Wildlife Trust. It was one of the ospreys from the Loch of the Lowes which gave me one of the most enjoyable bird-watching days I have experienced in more than thirty years of walking and hoping. It hovered over the still waters of the loch and then plunged down from a height of over ten metres (thirty feet) feet first to grab a large and protesting fish before rising on its powerful wings to a perch, where the fat trout was battered to death. Ospreys are able to hold on tight to their slippery and obviously protesting prey because of specially adapted rough scales on and around their toes, which function as a set of animated fishing hooks. Ospreys are between 50 and 60 centimetres (up to 24 inches) long and are dark on the back but with a white-crested head and pale underparts. They do, however, vary somewhat in plumage. They have an almost world-wide distribution and are found over a wider area than any other species except the barn owl. Such a large conspicuous bird as the osprey was not only thought to be a threat to fishing stocks but also had a good supply of commercially valuable feathers. They were thus bound to suffer once accurate guns became available. It is therefore no great surprise that the osprey became extinct as a British breeding species but one feature of its behaviour allowed the species to make a well publicised comeback – it is migratory, having its winter fishing grounds in Africa. Even

after they disappeared as a breeding population in the nineteenth century ospreys were sometimes sighted in Britain, but were quickly 'obtained' for private or museum collections. Fortunately the Scandinavian population was more than holding its own and it may well have been as the result of an overspill from this that in 1954 ospreys once more stood defiantly on an eyrie sited on the flat top of a Scots pine. It was 1958 before the Loch Garten pair successfully raised young. Any rarity in our over-selfish society has a price upon its head and British osprey eggs (how they could be distinguished from Scandinavian ones defeats me) were high on the shopping list of those unscrupulous egg collectors who think they are scientists and refer to themselves as oologists in the belief that it gives them respectability. We thus have the ridiculous situation reported in the *Daily Telegraph* of May 18th, 1971.

'Two youths were charged yesterday with stealing three rare osprey eggs from an eyrie at Loch Garten, Inverness-shire. It was discovered that the eggs were missing early yesterday morning after someone had been seen climbing down the tree which held the nest.

Volunteer wardens of the RSPB have been on a 24-hour security guard since the osprey's return to Loch Garten early in April.

The eyrie is situated on the top of a 40 ft tall pine tree, which is surrounded by a mass of barbed wire stretching from its base upwards for about 10 ft.

The tree is also fitted with electronic alarm warning devices but it is understood these were either by-passed or did not function. The young ospreys were due to hatch out in about seven to ten days time and it is feared they will not now survive.

"After this period of time away from the warmth of the female and the nest, everything would be against them," said a duty warden.

But despite the theft, the female osprey continued to sit on the nest yesterday and assisted the male in trying to rebuild the damaged eyrie.

Wardens also man a forward post near the tree during the night as an additional precaution. In 1958 the nest was robbed and hen eggs were substituted, since when a full-scale security operation has been mounted by the RSPB.

Since 1959, 23 young ospreys have been successfully reared at Loch Garten, and last year nearly 40,000 people visited the viewing post to see these rare fish hawks.

Other osprey have been sighted over a wide area of the Highlands and are nesting in the area, but the sites have not been disclosed.

Last year, three sites were occupied by osprey in Scotland, and eight young flew from them, the highest number for many decades. The total number of Scottish-bred birds reared since 1959 now stands at 37 including the 23 reared at Loch Garten

The two youths charged with theft are believed to be English.'

It is still a rather bizarre game, but the osprey in Scotland is now doing rather well and more than thirty eyries are now occupied, mostly sited in Scots pines close to water. Three eggs are usually laid during late April or early May, and although the male will take his turn most of the incubation is undertaken by the female and takes her about five weeks. During the two-month fledging period the male hunts for fish which he carries to the

female who tears up the prey and feeds it to the young, most of which have successfully completed their maiden flight by August. They can then join the adults on an often roundabout migratory journey, which may involve leisurely visits to Ireland, France, Spain and Portugal, where they have to run the gauntlet of 'sportsmen', before they reach their winter quarters in West Africa. Memories of their natal habitat seem to be embedded in the brain of the young birds and after an adolescence spent wandering they return at any time between the ages of three and six to breed themselves.

The divers

Whilst the larger lochs appeal to the ospreys, the red-throated divers prefer the smaller, shallower upland lochs, where their eerie calls echo through the highland mists or carry on the howling winds. Actually there are only four species of the primitive diver family still alive today and all are found in Europe and three of them – the great northern, the black-throated and the red-throated – have bred in Britain, the latter being the one most frequently encountered, although it is never common. In North America the family is also

Red-throated diver incubating.

present – including the fourth member, the white-billed diver – but there they are known as loons. The red-throated diver measures only 54–58 centimetres (about 22 inches) compared with the black-throated diver's 56–68 centimetres (up to 27 inches) and the great northern's comparatively bulky body of around 75 centimetres (30 inches). In the breeding season the throat colours from which both the smaller species derive their vernacular names separate them, but even in the greyer winter plumage the red-throated diver is a more slender-looking bird and has a slightly upturned bill which the experienced bird watcher can detect even in flight. Up to 1,000 pairs breed in Britain, but it will always be a difficult species to census because many of the small lochs on which it breeds are surrounded by bogs and blanketed by mist or curtained off by driving rain. These upland waters cannot support a rich bird life, unlike many of the lakes, tarns and reservoirs at lower altitudes which can support the rich and varied plant life on which the food chains depend.

Lakes, tarns and reservoirs

Lakes, tarns and reservoirs include waters which may be defined as oligotrophic, which means deficient in nutrients and therefore of plant and animal life. Some of Cumbria's upland tarns and lakes, most Welsh waters and some reservoirs used for drinking water fall into this category and in consequence are never rich in birds apart from when gulls use them as roosts or migrant wildfowl use them as resting places. On the other hand, reservoirs once used to provide canals with water to compensate for inevitable leakages, mill lodges, and lakes such as Coniston and Windermere are often rich in food and are said to be eutrophic. In many cases farm, domestic and holiday-time sewage fertilise the waters and a rich plant life develops quickly, providing both food and cover for birds. These waters are often popular with wildfowl such as the three species of swan, Canada geese, tufted duck and pochard.

Wildfowl is a term including 143 species of bird, of which 55 occur naturally in Britain.

Of these 55 we have 3 species of swan, 12 species of goose and the remaining 40 are ducks. Once a naturalist experiences the thrill of watching winter wildfowl he or she inevitably becomes addicted. One does not forget that it is cold work, but it makes the discomfort bearable. The sound of truly wild geese 'whiffling' down out of a heavy December sky, the drone of powerful wings, the honking of a skein of geese in flight, the lonely whistle of a wigeon and the sheer grace of a spring of teal are sights and sounds never to be forgotten.

Mute swan *(Cygnus olor)*,
Whooper swan *(Cygnus cygnus)*
and Bewick's swan *(Cygnus bewickii)*
To many people a swan is just a swan, but to Britain's winter bird watchers there are three distinct species to look out for. From October onwards we have the resident mute swan, joined by two visitors from the cold lands of the north. The visitors tend to be much more gregarious and vocal. The also tend to hold their necks much straighter than the mute swan, which keeps its neck in an S shape for much of the time. One of the visitors is the whooper swan which at 150 centimetres (60 inches) is the same size as the mute swan. The other is the much smaller Bewick's swan, which is only 120 centimetres (48 inches) long. I think that the easiest way to dis-

Whooper swan – note yellow pointed patch on bill (**left**).
Bewick's swan – note yellow patch ends bluntly (**right**).

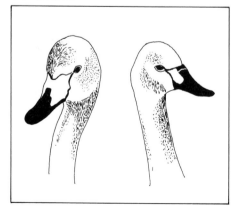

Mute swans' nests are often damaged by vandals.

Whooper swans are usually accompanied on migration by their cygnets.

Whooper swans at the Wildfowl Trust Reserve at Martin Mere, Lancashire.

tinguish between the three species is by careful examination of the colour of the bills. That of the mute swan is black and orange, with a prominent knob at the base of the male bird's bill. Both the whooper and Bewick's swan have bills of black and yellow, but the distribution of the colours is different enough to make distinction between them quite easy. There is more yellow on the bill of the whooper swan and the yellow pigment ends in a sharp point. There is much less yellow on the bill of the Bewick's and the pigment ends bluntly. This you may find hard to remember, but it may make it easier if you think that B is the first letter in Bewick's and also the first letter in blunt.

Both species make a lot of noise, but these calls are vital to them as they fly on migration, for this is the language by which each bird, flying at something like 80 kilometres (50 miles) per hour, keeps in contact with its neighbour. The whooper swan breeds in Iceland, Scandinavia, Russia and northern Asia. Bewick's swans, on the other hand, are restricted in their breeding habitat to Arctic Russia and Siberia. Their long migratory journeys are not without hazard from both inclement weather and inconsiderate people. Investigations carried out by the Wildfowl Trust have shown that swans captured for ringing and weighing often contain considerable quantities of lead shot. This has been discovered by the rather expensive procedure of X-raying a proportion of the captured birds. Similar investigations on mute swans have shown that they too are not immune from unscrupulous shooters who range over our shrinking countryside, but there is a great deal of evidence to show that many swans and other dabbling wildfowl are killed by the lead in fishing weights.

Lead poisoning

A report to goverment published in December 1981 by the Nature Conservancy Council called for the voluntary phasing out

1 Long-eared owl.

2 Golden eagle (**above**).　　　　　　　3 Sparrow-hawk (**below**).

4 Common redstart (male) (**above**).   5 Common redstart (female) (**below**).

8 Kingfisher.

6 Waxwing (**opposite above**).

7 Greenfinch (**opposite**).

9 Moorhen (**above**).   10 Great crested grebe (**below**).

11 Coot (**above**).

12 Barnacle goose (**below**).

15 Kestrel.

13 Dotterel (male) (**opposite above**).

14 Linnet (**opposite**).

16 Little ringed plover (**above**).   17 Oystercatcher (**below**).

18 Eider duck (**above**).   19 Chough (**below**).

22 Kittiwakes.

20 Manx shearwater (**opposite above**).

21 Gannets (**opposite**).

23 Shag.

24 Razorbill (**opposite above**).

25 Guillemots (**opposite**).

26 Puffin.

of lead weights in angling within five years and immediate action meanwhile to reduce the effects of lead, especially split shot. The report recommends that the situation be reviewed in 1984 and that if lead is then found to be still widely in use further consideration should be given to securing its phasing out in angling.

The report showed conclusively that large numbers of swans are dying as a result of lead poisoning due to the ingestion of fishing weights, especially split lead shot. It is estimated that 250 tonnes of lead is introduced into the environment each year in the form of lead shot – an equivalent of two pieces of shot per foot per annum along all lowland rivers and canals. Mute swans feed mainly on submerged aquatic vegetation and require grit to aid their digestion. Discarded lead shot on river banks and in water may be mistaken for grit and once swallowed causes death by starvation as the lead affects the nervous system, preventing the normal functions of the gizzard. During the eighteen months prior to the publication of the report, examinations of 288 dead swans found throughout Britain have shown that lead poisoning was by far the largest single cause of death, accounting for 39·2%. The problem is, however, particularly acute on certain rivers, notably the Trent, the Warwickshire Avon and the Thames, where there has been a marked decline in the number of swans over the past ten or fifteen years. On these rivers, 75% to 90% of swan deaths were due to lead poisoning over the period from 1973 to 1981. In such areas the substantial decline in immature birds resulting from lead poisoning can be expected to have a marked effect on future swan populations. By contrast, very few cases of lead poisoning have been recorded in Scotland, where coarse fishing using lead shot is less prevalent. The report estimates that in England alone between 2,700 and 3,500 swans may be dying each year from lead poisoning. Swan deaths from lead poisoning appear to be higher on water poor in aquatic plant life – which may, in some places, be the result of heavy boat traffic. This can be a real problem on inland waters used for both boating and fishing.

The main recommendations set out in the report are:

The Code of Practice for anglers, developed by the National Anglers' Council, should be given maximum publicity in tackle shops, angling clubs, etc.

'No fishing' zones should be designated in problem areas (as in the centres of Reading and Stratford) to enable swan numbers to recover.

The use of split-lead shot should be phased out within five years. In the meantime acceptable alternatives should be developed and marketed (the Council has already instigated research into 'tungsten putty') and anglers should be encouraged to use existing non-toxic alternatives such as steel pin weights.

Manufacturers should develop and market alternative ledger, spinning and sea-fishing weights composed of non-toxic materials. The NCC should review the position in 1984 and should lead be found at that time to be still widely in use then further consideration should be given to securing its phasing out in angling.

Where practicable, attempts should be made to clear lead from heavily fished areas; grit should be provided in grit-deficient areas where swans at risk are known to feed; and monitoring of lead levels in live swans should be extended.

We must all hope that these measures come into operation and that we continue to protect the mute swan which has enjoyed a longer period of protection in Britain than any other species. Indeed, it has been so well protected that it has almost, but not quite, become domesticated. Its flesh was so good to eat that it was preserved for the rich and influential. These people were granted the right to mark the bills of the swans they captured during the annual swan-upping ceremonies. Any unmarked birds were said to belong to the sovereign. The oldest of these swan marks dates back to 1482, but perhaps the most interesting to modern readers is the mark belonging to the Vintners' Company. They were permitted to scratch two nicks on the bill in the shape of an inverted V. This 'swan with two nicks' has become corrupted slightly and is depicted in the inn sign 'The Swan with Two Necks'. Thus one sees what is apparently a double-headed swan, which is obviously much more arresting than one with two slight nicks on its bill.

Canada goose *Branta canadensis*

In contrast with the mute swan the Canada goose is finding the present day environment very much to its liking. It is a handsome bird being some 96 centimetres (36 inches) long. It has a brownish body and a black head with a patch of white on its chin. The legs and the bill are black. Some ornithologists state that the Canada goose has not been resident in Britain for very long. This I find rather difficult to comprehend since the species is mentioned by a writer called Willoughby in 1678, when he counted the king's wildfowl in St James's Park, London. It has been a regular if fairly rare breeding species for over 300 years. In recent years it has increased quite dramatically and flocks of over 700 birds have been recorded during the winter months at Tatton Park in Cheshire and large flocks now occur in many other areas. The nest is constructed on the ground and usually near water. It is lined with weeds and soft grey down. The goose alone incubates the four to ten greenish eggs. The proud and fierce gander stands close by and permits nothing to approach without a fight. The eggs hatch in about a month and the goslings can fly about six weeks after hatching.

Canada geese in Britain are tamer than in their natural habitat (North America) and until recent times have not shown any tendency to migrate. The migratory habit, however, does now seem to be evolving and large numbers of English birds travel to north-eastern Scotland to moult. Thus it would seem that migration may not be totally instinctive but is still in the process of evolving in some species. There is also plenty of evidence to suggest that in recent years Britain and western Europe have been experiencing wetter, cooler summers, although the winters are milder, giving an overall situation of higher average temperatures. It is,

however, the cooler summers which seem to have persuaded more and more ducks to remain here to breed, a behaviour pattern well illustrated by the tufted duck and pochard.

Non-scientific classification of ducks

Ducks are often divided by bird watchers into three groups called diving ducks, dabbling ducks and sawbills. Diving ducks such as the tufted duck dive beneath the water surface for their food. Dabbling ducks such as the teal and the mallard merely dip their bills into the water or upend their bodies to reach deeper. They never dive whilst feeding and the only occasion which may cause them to dive is when they are attempting to escape from a predator. The sawbills, as we have seen in the case of the red-breasted merganser and the goosander, are a very specialised group of diving ducks which feed on fish. The third member of the family found in Britain is the smew, which can often be seen on lowland lakes and reservoirs. The male is often called the 'white nun', from his plumage, but I cannot help feeling that 'white monk' would be a more sensible name for a drake. The female is dull brown but the small size of the species – 40 centimetres (16 inches) for the male with the duck slightly smaller – and her reddish head makes the species easily recognised. The smew, however, is never common and does not breed in Britain.

Tufted duck *Aythya fuligula*

Like many of the diving ducks, the tufted can remain under water for quite some time, and an inquiring naturalist can add interest to the day by timing these dives. I once timed a drake tufted diving and recorded 27, 25, 27, 26 and 25 seconds. There was less than 5 seconds delay between the completion of one dive and the beginning of the next. This exercise can often be done more efficiently by two people, one of whom watches whilst the other records. All who take their hobby seriously should keep a diary recording their observations. Diving times, for example, can often help to identify a bird, especially when distance or adverse lighting conditions pre-

vent accurate observation of plumage details. In recent years many wildfowl in Britain have shown an increasing tendency to remain with us and breed. The tufted duck is a good example of this. Whilst the majority of the population are still migrants increasing numbers are becoming part of our resident population, which is now around 7,000 pairs.

The tufted duck likes building its nest on small islands or in wet areas close to water. The eggs are a light shade of green and the clutch size varies from six to fourteen. Only the duck incubates and it takes her about 25 days of patient sitting before the black-and-yellow ducklings peck their way out. The young birds actually smash the shell by striking upwards and backwards with the bill, which has a special protrusion on the upper mandible to assist in this task. It is possessed by most species of bird and is appropriately called the egg tooth. It falls off within a day or two after hatching. The male tufted duck is indeed a handsome fellow, being mainly shining black but with a white rectangle on his flanks. Set into his dark head is a bright

Tufted drake – the breeding population of this species is rising steadily in Britain.

yellow eye. The tuft on the head which gives the species its name is not always obvious except in a breeze. The tufted duck is occasionally confused with the goldeneye, another diving duck. The two are quite different, really, because the goldeneye has a white patch beneath the eye and this stands out like a beacon even from great distances. The female tufted duck is very much browner and duller than her mate, but she can be recognised by the blue bill which is characteristic of the species.

Pochard *Aythya ferina*

The pochard is about 46 centimetres (18½ inches) long and is some 2·5 centimetres (1 inch) longer than the tufted duck, but the former is a much heavier-looking bird. The drake is easily recognised by his lovely chestnut-coloured head and neck, greyish-white body and shiny black chest. The females are, as usual, much duller and have a brownish head, neck and breast which do, however, stand out clearly from the paler underparts and there is an easily seen blue band across the bill. Far fewer pochards breed in Britain than tufted ducks and it is in the winter that the two are likely to come into competition, but this event is largely avoided by the fact that the pochard is more of a vegetarian and the tufted duck takes more animal matter and also seems more willing to accept smaller stretches of water than the pochard. Tufted ducks are therefore found on smaller ponds, habitats often rich in birds and to which we now turn our attention.

Ponds

With the ever-increasing demand for land, improved water supplies, larger farm units and more emphasis on both arable and factory farming, the farm pond has often become redundant. Where larger ponds are still present the aggressive coot will be found competing successfully for its own niche along with the smaller but more adaptable moorhen.

Coot *Fulica atra*

The coot measures some 37·5 centimetres (15 inches) and has a very conspicuous white frontal shield and bill which contrast sharply with the black plumage, although there is a narrow white border on the wing which shows up clearly in flight. It is a larger, more thick-set bird than the moorhen and also tends to be more gregarious as well as demanding more marginal cover for breeding. Even the nests made up of piles of aquatic vegetation tend to be semicolonial and I once found eight nests within the confines of a pond just less than 1 acre in area. Both sexes build the nest and the first eggs are usually laid in April. Both sexes share the 23-day incubation period of the 6–10 eggs (occasionally as many as 15), which are buff-coloured and dotted with spots of dark brown. Within four days of hatching the young have left the nest and the brood seems to be divided into two, each parent taking charge of half the young. Two broods are often raised and on the odd occasion three broods are raised, which means that adults with non-flying young can often be observed as late as November.

In the main the diet of the coot consists of vegetation, but they will take the occasional mollusc or perhaps a fish now and again. In recent years a peculiar feeding relationship has been observed between wildfowl, especially geese, and coots. Grass is very difficult to digest and an analysis of the droppings of barnacle and pink-footed geese has shown that less than 50% of the available food material has been extracted. Coots have been observed following the geese and eating their droppings, thus tapping a most valuable source of semi-digested food. This habit is no more revolting and just as efficient as a cow chewing the cud. It has been estimated that between 50,000 and 100,000 coots breed in Britain and this compares with an estimated 300,000 pairs of moorhens.

Moorhen *Gallinula chloropus*

The male moorhen builds several platforms of reeds and defends the territory around them from other males. He then takes the female on a sort of tour of inspection and one site is selected which the male, assisted by the female, completes. The clutch size varies from five to eleven eggs but as many as twenty-one have been recorded no doubt due to two females using the same nest. The ground colour is greenish-buff liberally covered with spots and blotches of rusty brown. Both sexes incubate the eggs for about three weeks and it was during the period of two or three days in which the young remain in the nest that I once observed a most unusual occurrence.

In the grounds of a small town park four young moorhens were being brooded when suddenly the parents began to dismantle the nest and rebuild it at a higher level above the water surface. An hour later it began to rain so heavily that the water level rose dramatically. The following morning dawned dry and clear and bathed in warm sunlight the dutiful parents once more dismantled the nest and rebuilt it on the original site. It would seem from this evidence that moorhens and probably all birds are able to detect weather changes, possibly by the ears being sensitive to atmospheric pressure. This phenomenon has

since been investigated by Norman Elkins. The diet of the moorhen appears superficially to be similar to that of the coot, but competition is avoided by the former often feeding away from water on slugs, on earthworms, and often on young woodland birds taken from the nest. Moorhens, despite their rather clockwork-looking walk, are actually quite accomplished climbers and do pose quite a threat to fledging birds, which explains why small birds mob a moorhen strolling through a wood with just as much gusto as that applied to an owl. There is no doubt that the draining of ponds has been detrimental to moorhens, but what is lost on the swings is gained on the roundabouts and the next three habitats show that human activities can be beneficial to bird life.

The moorhen – often not the little innocent bird which its appearance suggests.

Canals

The initial effect of canal construction on wildlife cannot have been beneficial but in those days there was a great deal of country-side and the birds would have found no trouble in adapting. During the busy days of canals few birds would have been able to use them for breeding, but with the coming of the railways the disused canals became the haven for wildlife which they still are. Even the increasing numbers of holiday craft have not affected the goodly populations of dabchick, coot, moorhens, mute swans and the ever-present mallard.

Mallard *Anas platyrhynchos*

It would be wrong to write off this beautiful species as a farmyard duck since it is a truly wild bird and many individuals are capable of very long migratory journeys. The mallard is the most common duck in Britain with up to 300,000 breeding pairs, and a population swelling to more than 2 million birds in winter. It is also the largest British duck, measuring 58 centimetres (23 inches). The male is a most spectacular bird. The only reason he does not receive the acclaim he deserves is the fact that he is so common and familiarity, in ornithology as elsewhere, breeds contempt. The lovely shimmering green head, white neck band and bright yellow bill along with a rusty breast and grey body are a joy to behold, especially on a bright frosty morning. The female, as usual, is duller but can be identified by the speculum, a bright purple patch on the wing. In his eclipse (non-breeding) plumage the male is dull, but he can be distinguished by the curled tail feathers, also typical of the breeding plumage.

The mallard has two peaks of display prior to breeding, the first as early as October and November and the second during February and March. The British population may start nest building as early as March and I once found a duck incubating a clutch of seven eggs on March 1st. The nest is constructed by the duck, usually in thick cover at the edge of the water but occasionally in the hollow of a tree. She may even take over the old nest of a crow or even the domed structure of a magpie, but does take the trouble to line it with feathers. The clutch size varies between six and sixteen eggs but an average would be about ten. The female incubates them for about a month and she also takes sole charge of the young until they fly, some two months after hatching. In cases where the nest is some distance from the water the family walk there together and I once followed a duck and ten ducklings along the King's Road to Chelsea Bridge and down the steps to the Thames. At one point a friendly London copper held up the traffic to allow the ducks to cross the road safely. Further north, on the Leeds to Liverpool canal near Gargrave, I counted seven mallard nests along a two-mile stretch of bank.

Flashes

Flashes are areas of still water caused by the flooding of old mine workings. Round Sandbach in Cheshire flashes were formed when areas of land beneath which salt had been extracted filled up with water, and later reeds thrived around the edges. Pennington Flash near Leigh and the RSPB reserve at Fairburn Ings near Castleford formed as a result of coal-mining subsidence. There are many other examples in Wales, Scotland and Northumberland, and in Cumbria iron-ore mines have similarly caused flooding and produced a fantastically rich habitat, often assisted by amateur conservationists planting native trees and water plants. These make the perfect habitat for many of the wetland species already described but three other beneficiaries have been the heron, the shoveller and the ruddy duck.

Heron *Ardea cinerea*

The heron is such a large, conspicuous bird that its 8,000 breeding pairs are easily censused, a task made considerably easier by their sedentary nature and a tendency to nest in large traditional heronries. Breeding begins early in the year and the clutch of about four blue eggs are being incubated by the time the spring equinox brings the promise of warm weather. Incubation, which takes about a month, is shared by the sexes, the males apparently taking the day shift whilst the females take over for the night.

A hunting heron is a fascinating sight. The gaunt grey figure of the 90 centimetre (36 inch) tall heron stays still until prey, usually fish, water voles or frogs, is sighted and then it moves with surprising speed to stab and lift the victim. Eels are a favourite food and a fierce battle often occurs as a hungry heron struggles to subdue a protesting fish. At the end of the often protracted performance the heron is often covered with slime. It has a very ingenious method of dealing with this. The feathers on its flank turn to powder when struck by the bill. This powder down is spread on the slime and soaks it up so that all the heron has to do is to scrape off the mixture with its toe, wash its feet, preen the feathers

A grey heron patiently fishing.

and all is set for the next meal. Maintaining waterproof plumage is very important to all water birds and herons, like wildfowl, have an oil gland (called a uropygial gland) which poultry eaters will know as the parson's nose. Such a gland is also important to dabbling ducks such as the shoveler.

Shoveler *Anas clypeata*
The shoveller is one of those species which thoroughly deserves its name for who could call its huge flat bill anything other than a shovel? The green head of the 50 centimetre (20 inch) drake is very like that of a mallard but the white chest and large expanse of chestnut on the sides are quite clear. With the ducks, however, the distinction is not so easily made but the sheer size of the bill plus the fact that the speculum of the shoveler is green and not purple as in the mallard makes the task of separating the two fairly easy to the experienced bird watcher. At one time it was thought that the shoveler was resident but ringing returns have shown that two distinct

populations are found in Britain. Flocks pour into Britain from northern Europe for the winter and they return to the breeding grounds in the spring and are replaced by about 1,000 pairs of summer visitors arriving from France and Spain during February. These birds breed from May onwards, when a clutch of around ten eggs is laid and incubated by the female for just over three weeks. The male does not help to incubate, but he does remain in the vicinity of his mate and can be aggressively territorial.

Ruddy duck *Oxyura jamaicensis*
Some of the artificial habitats, especially those in Cheshire, have proved useful not only to naturally occurring species but also to introduced species such as the ruddy duck, which hails from North America. The first record of ruddy ducks escaping and breeding in Britain was in 1960 and since then W. H. Hudson has estimated that the population has

The ruddy duck — now becoming more common in Britain after escaping from collections.

The shoveler's bill is used to filter food from the water.

been rising at the rate of 25% per annum, a phenomenal rate of increase, and 800 birds are now at liberty in Britain. It is a small duck, measuring only 40 centimetres (16 inches), but the male is easily distinguished by his reddish flanks and back with a blue head and bill plus prominent white cheeks. Even in eclipse plumage this latter feature distinguishes the male from his mate, as do his long stiff tail feathers. Usually these stiff tail feathers are held horizontally but during display they are held and waved like a banner. There is a very peculiar display pattern in which the male cocks his tail feathers and raised feathers on his head which look like horns, a specialised air sac in the neck is inflated and a tune is played by drumming upon it with the bill. Sometimes the bill is held close to the water and the burping bubbling call produced is unique to the ruddy duck.

Gravel pits

In one sense gravel pits are similar to mining flashes, but the digging can be more carefully controlled, and because of pressure from conservation groups many companies have welcomed expert help with regard to landscaping. Harrison did some wonderful work in the 1960s at a gravel pit near Sevenoaks and several floating islands were constructed on which water birds readily nested. It was also discovered that a circular pit attracted only one pair of mallards whilst one with a series of inlets into which territorially minded males could move and be invisible to rivals increased the breeding stock dramatically. Such gravel pits have also helped to increase significantly the breeding populations of great crested grebes, and also of little ringed plovers.

Great crested grebe *Podiceps cristatus*
Like the heron, the great crested grebe is a very conspicuous bird and as such is a very easy bird to census. It was almost extinct at the beginning of this century. This was due to its most attractive plumage which was in great demand by the millinery trade. The body measures 46 centimetres (18 inches) and

the head is carried on a long slender neck. In winter the back is dark grey and the under parts creamy-white. The crown and ear tufts are dark and a white line over the eye is clearly visible. The breeding plumage is indeed splendid and one can appreciate the milliners' love for 'grebe skins'. There are long chestnut feathers on the side of the face which form a frill called the tippet, which looks just like an Elizabethan ruff. This is set off brilliantly against the ear tufts, pink bill and crimson eyes. All these features are shared by both sexes, which indulge in one of the most impressive courtship displays in the whole of the bird world. They dive together, run over the water together, and exchange water weed as a sort of engagement present before building the large nest from the same material. Emergent vegetation is essential for the anchorage of the nest and once this is built, usually in May, three or four chalky-white eggs are laid and incubated by both sexes for about a month. The incubating bird is wary and before leaving the eggs it covers them with weed and then slips quietly off the nest and swims away under water. The parents really do take care of their striped youngsters, which can often be seen riding around on the backs of the adults. The diet of the great crested grebes consists mainly of fish, but they do seem to eat a lot of feathers – including their own – and it is thought that these may prevent fish bones damaging the gut. The bones are probably wrapped in the feathers and regurgitated as a soft pellet.

However much we may congratulate ourselves on providing habitats for birds such as the great crested grebe we cannot escape the fact that the Britain of today holds but a mere fraction of the water birds it once held and species such as the spoonbill are now extinct here. Should we be ashamed? I think not, since the swamps and shallows which sheltered Hereward the Wake and other rebels were breeding grounds not only for birds and mammals but for small and dangerous beasts such as the mosquito, which carried the malarial parasite which was rampant in Britain of the Middle Ages. We have long since accepted that a place for man is vital and

Great crested grebe – once hunted nearly to extinction for its lovely coloured feathers.

have used all our ingenuity to bring this about. What we have to do now is to ensure that we provide a place for birds by creating new habitat as described above but also retaining important wetland areas such as the Norfolk Broads, the Somerset Levels, Leighton Moss on the border of North Lancashire and Cumbria, and the Cambridge-shire Washes.

The wetlands

All these areas are rich in birds and it is here that the avocet, black tern and black-tailed godwit have returned to breed among the resident water birds. Two species in particular typify these threatened areas. These are the bittern and bearded tit.

Bittern   *Botaurus stellaris*

Once so common that it was a regular item on the diet of the fenmen, the bittern died out at the end of the nineteenth century, recovered from about 1916, but has declined a little recently and only about 40 pairs now breed. This is a great pity for this hunchbacked rusty-looking member of the heron family whose booming call echoes for miles over the reedbeds is one of our most engaging species. The bittern measures some 75 centimetres (30 inches) and feeds upon small mammals, birds, fish and frogs plus a few invertebrates and a small quantity of vegetable matter. It often shares its habitat with the marsh harrier (*Circus aeruginosus*), of which fewer than thirty pairs breed in reedbeds of Britain. Could this 55 centimetre (22 inch) predator, the largest of the harrier family, be a problem for young bitterns? It would seem that the reverse is true and young harriers standing on

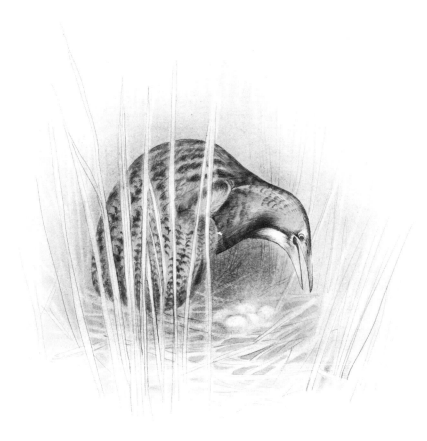

The bittern is still suffering from diminishing habitat.

Young marsh harrier prepares to defend itself.

The water rail — one of Britain's shyest birds.

Opposite (left)
Reed warbler on its nest slung cleverly between marshland vegetation.

Opposite (right)
As many as 300,000 sedge warblers still breed in the reed beds of Britain.

Right
Bearded reedling (female).

Below
Bearded reedling (male).

top of their nest of sticks and reeds are often taken by hunting bitterns. Obviously larger areas of reedbeds are needed if the two species are to survive; other birds also need more living space, including sedge and reed warblers, water rails, and that most delightful little bird the bearded tit.

Bearded tit *Panurus biarmicus*

The bearded tit is a fascinating species to the bird biologist since it shows how both habitat and weather can affect populations. About 500 pairs breed in Britain but numbers are reduced by loss of habitat and spells of cold weather. Recent work on the species – which does not belong to the tit family and is better classed as a reedling – shows a remarkable adaptation to help it cope with cold weather. Low temperatures can be a problem for the bearded tit, which is related to the babblers – a tropical family. There is no problem finding food in the summer reedbeds when insects abound, but do bearded tits eat reed seeds during the winter as Victorian naturalists suggested? This idea was discounted until it was found that in the winter a dramatic change occurs in the structure of the gizzard of this delightful little bird. A delicate gizzard is quite adequate to grind up soft-bodied insects, but to deal with tough seeds the gizzard becomes thick and muscular. This condition remains until December but after this time a spell of really mild weather may bring about the return to the summer

gizzard. A cold spell after this event has taken place can be disastrous to the bearded tit population and they are therefore able to withstand a freeze before January but probably not after February.

The basic colour of bearded tits is a bright tawny brown and even a superficial glance at the head of the male will reveal differences from the long-tailed tit, the only British species with which it can be confused. The head is a delicate lavender-grey and there is an easily seen glossy black moustachial stripe. The bill is clear yellow and whilst the female is duller and lacks the moustachial stripe the tiny 9 centimetre (just over 3½ inch) body plus the 7 centimetre (nearly 3 inch) tail is still easily identified. The nest is built low down in the reeds by both sexes. Both also share in the incubation of the clutch of eggs, which can reach twelve in number though half this total is the average size. The young emerge in about 12 or 13 days and after being fed by both parents the young fly in the remarkably short time of 9–12 days. It is no wonder that the losses of the winter can quickly be made good as three broods are often raised during a breeding season which may begin as early as April and continue into August.

Here again we find a simple answer to what seems to be a complex question. What shall we do to ensure the survival of rare species? The answer is to do nothing except preserve the environment in which the species lives and then let it fend for itself.

Opposite
Long-tailed tits build a most intricate nest full of feathers.

7 Mountain, Moor and Heath

In 1983 the Countryside Commission published a booklet called *What Future for the Uplands?* which considered the character of the upland countryside of England and Wales. The findings apply equally well to Scotland and, for that matter, anywhere else in Europe. The problem is often too many people in the wrong place at the wrong time. Clearly a balance must be struck between ski-lifts and highland birds, walkers and moorland species and picnic sites plus the inevitable property developers and the birds of the lowland heaths. All upland and heathland areas are under threat, and their birds can be conveniently considered in three groups: birds of the mountain, birds of moorland managed for grouse, and finally birds of lowland heaths will be considered.

Mountain birds

It is in the mountains of Britain that some of our rarest birds are to be found although whether this is by choice is open to debate. At one time before the advent of accurate firearms and lethal poisons the peregrine, the raven and the golden eagle were relatively common birds, even in lowland Britain where the odd crag jutted out above an unspoiled river valley. A look at an old Ordnance Survey map will reveal Eagle crags, Falcon cliffs and Raven hills in places now humming with the buzz of traffic and the roar of disco music. The dotterel, too, has been substantially reduced by man's greed and only that splendid mountain grouse the ptarmigan may be said to have remained in its primeval home. A look at the life of, and problems faced by, these five species will enable us to appreciate what we have done and are doing to this habitat.

Peregrine *Falco peregrinus*
Judging by the number of cases brought before the courts and the press space given to

it the lovely peregrine falcon is Britain's most controversial bird. An article by Brian Jackman in the *Sunday Times* of August 14th, 1983, commenting on an RSPB press release, illustrates this:

'NET FAILS TO SAVE FALCONS
A furious row is about to break out between the Royal Society for the Protection of Birds and the Department of the Environment.

The cause: the peregrine falcon, a bird which has been described as the ultimate flying machine, and avidly sought after by falconers.

Britain is now the centre of a lucrative black market in stolen birds, with West Germans and Arabs among those prepared to pay up to £1,500 for one.

Protection for peregrines and other birds of prey should have been tightened last September with the compulsory registration and ringing of captive birds of prey under the new Wildlife and Countryside Act.

Instead, according to the society, 72 peregrine eyries have been robbed this year, making 1983 the worst year on record.

"The government's scheme to protect the peregrine is nothing but a bureaucratic rubber stamp that is condoning crime," says Ian Presst, the society's director. "It will remain a sham."

By imposing maximum fines of £1,000 for stealing a wild peregrine or its egg and enforcing registration of captive birds, it was hoped that the threat to Britain's 350 breeding pairs would be controlled.

"With an average clutch of four eggs to a nest," says Presst, "the plundering of 72 eyries could represent as many as 280 wild peregrines, taken either as eggs to be hatched in an incubator, or as young birds to be put into aviaries to dupe government inspectors with false claims of captive breeding."

It is difficult to breed peregrines in

The peregrine population in Britain is now recovering.

captivity, but by the end of July, 253 eggs had been registered as having been laid in captivity this year.

What has particularly angered the society is the introduction of general licences allowing the sale not only of captive-bred peregrines, but also golden eagles, merlins, and ever rarer birds such as goshawks, ospreys, red kites and honey buzzards.'

Evidence suggests that 1984 was not likely

to be much better, but the 750 pairs still breeding in Britain must be protected. During the nineteenth century the species was persecuted by gamekeepers, who saw the peregrine, not without some justification, as a flying slaughterhouse. The peregrine, however, probably takes few game birds but concentrates on pigeons and gulls. It was this partiality to pigeons which led to the official government policy at the start of the Second World War which was to destroy peregrines in case they killed a homing pigeon carrying a vital message. The species is still not popular with pigeon fanciers but in truth the birds are

The wheatear, a common summer visitor to upland Britain, is often an important part of the peregrine's prey.

now sufficiently few in number not to be a threat. The final reduction in numbers has been due to hydrocarbon insecticides and herbicides already discussed in relation to the sparrow-hawk, and latterly to the attentions of unscrupulous collectors.

The female measures 48 centimetres (19 inches) and is 10 centimetres (4 inches) larger than her mate, for which reason she is called the falcon and her mate the tiercel, a not very accurate Norman word which means 'one third' smaller. The peregrine is the largest British falcon and very formidable it looks as it sweeps through the air, wings swept back and beating in a manner which makes it resemble an overgrown pigeon. It is only when at rest that the full beauty of its plumage may be seen. The upper plumage is dark blue-grey with the underparts much paler but barred with black. The sides of the head and the crown are black as is the moustachial stripe, which gives the bird a vaguely oriental appearance. Apart from her size, the female is invariably darker than her mate. Peregrines

catch their prey on the wing and therefore need wide open spaces to search for and capture food, especially during the extended breeding season. Three or four eggs, orange-red blotched with brown, are usually laid in a traditional eyrie (which also makes the birds vulnerable). They are incubated mainly by the female for about a month. The male does occasionally sit on the eggs but he spends most of his time hunting for himself and his mate. She often rises from the eyrie to greet the hunter and the prey is then passed from foot to foot in a most exciting manner. Once the eggs have hatched the young are very demanding and both parents are hard-pressed to find enough for them to eat, especially in a hard winter.

Raven *Corvus corax*

The raven shares this demanding habitat, but seems to have less trouble in harsh winters than the more efficient killer, the peregrine. This is because the raven is tough and is also a carrion feeder. In bad winters many animals die, including deer, sheep and birds. The raven seems to have great resistance, stays alive longer, and then feasts upon the dead. Both male and female ravens are uniformly

Raven.

black, but when struck by sunlight a slightly greenish-blue gloss can be detected. It is the largest passerine species, being 62 centimetres (24½ inches) long and weighing up to 1 kilogram (2¼ pounds). Passerines are also called 'songbirds', but it is perhaps being too kind to describe the deep 'pruk-pruk' or the guttural 'clocking' sounds of the raven as a song. Ravens pair for life and are faithful to their nest site for many years, a factor which – just as with the peregrine and the eagle – has led to their downfall in a world dominated by man. Often as early as February the walker in the highlands may be treated to a display of raven aerobatics which marks the onset of the breeding season, during which time a huge nest of twigs lined with wool is built and filled with a clutch of from three to six eggs, which the female incubates for three weeks. During this time she is fed by the male from his throat pouch and he also helps her to feed the young. The young are able to fly when they are about 45 days old but the family remain together for several months, only breaking up prior to the next breeding season. Obviously with this degree of parental care there is time for only one brood to be raised and population increases will be slow. The present British breeding population of about 5,000 pairs is not likely to rise very quickly, although some extension of range is becoming more apparent in these more enlightened times – a feature also apparent in the golden eagle.

Golden eagle *Aquila chrysaetos*
This bird is known to all but recognised by few. It is often confused with the much smaller buzzard, with which it often shares this upland habitat. Both the buzzard and the eagle, like the raven, often fare best in hard winters when there is plenty of carrion about. The eagle is Britain's most splendid bird, looking as if fashioned from beaten brass as it

The golden eagle has made a spectacular comeback during this century.

soars about on thermals of air or sails gracefully along with the wind. The size varies from 75 to 90 centimetres (30–36 inches), and with a mighty wingspan of about 2 metres (6–7 feet) the birds are impressive indeed. There is no difference in the plumage of the two sexes but the females are often considerably larger than their mates. At present rather more than 300 pairs breed in Britain all – with the exception of two or three pairs in the Lake District – in Scotland. The Lake District birds need to be left in peace and so long as dieldrin- and aldrin-based chemicals are kept under control the range is likely to increase still further. The eyrie is constructed by both sexes. The structure is very bulky but kept surprisingly tidy and decorated regularly with fresh greenery. The odd nest is sited in a tree but these days most are on cliff edges. The usual clutch is of two eggs which have a creamy base heavily spotted and blotched with brown, and incubation is usually well under way by the end of March. This early start is essential and both sexes share the long task, which takes 45 days. Incubation begins with the first egg which means that one of the youngsters is more powerful than the other. Should food become short the fate of the weaker is sealed and you have one well fed youngster! The fledging period is about 80 days, which means that only one brood can be attempted and breeding must being early. The displaying eagles often have the high tops entirely to themselves, although in Scotland they sometimes have ptarmigans for company.

Ptarmigan *Lagopus mutus*

The ptarmigan is really a mountain grouse, measuring 35 centimetres (14 inches). In many ways it is the most remarkable bird of all those found in the Highlands and the only one which possesses a winter plumage and simply sits in snowdrifts and waits for conditions to improve. Some workers have suggested that it survives partly because of the wonderful insulation given by its down feathers – even the legs are feathered – but recent work suggests that the ptarmigan is able to reduce its heart-rate, blood pressure and respiration. This means that the ptarmigan is in a sort of suspended animation and that hibernation, however temporary, may well be possible. In winter the plumage is pure white save for a black tail and the male at this time also has black lores (the area between the base of the bill and the eye). The wings and underparts remain white at all seasons, but there are also distinct autumn and summer plumages, making three changes each year. In autumn the male is grey barred with black, while the female is a much softer brown. In summer the male is dark brown coarsely spotted and lined with even darker shades, and the female can be distinguished by a yellow colour and a much less prominent red wattle. Like most of the grouse family a prominent display area is essential and male ptarmigans stand on boulders first to attract mates and

Ptarmigan in winter plumage.

then to survey the scene (or perhaps keep guard) while the females incubate the clutch of five to ten eggs over a period of just over three weeks. At first the chicks, which are striped and perfectly camouflaged against the rocks, are looked after by the female while the cock birds gather in flocks. After a while the males condescend to return to their families and at this time they often share the habitat with the dotterel.

Dotterel *Eudromias morinellus*

The dotterel has a most confiding nature and this has helped its decline, though climatic changes may also have been a factor. Now that it is rare, the silly activities of bird watchers can affect it, as is shown by a story carried by the *Daily Telegraph* on May 27th, 1975:

‘DOTTEREL'S HOLIDAY WEEKEND
A pair of dotterel, Highland birds of the plover family, which are rapidly vanishing from Britain, have astonished birdwatchers on the North Norfolk coast by wandering tamely within yards of them.

Normally about 150 dotterel nest in Britain. They are to be seen in "trips" (or groups) above 2,500 ft in the Cairngorms and Highlands.

Their numbers have been diminishing over the last 30 years, mainly because of looting by egg collectors; they have rarely been seen in England or Wales.

They raise families among the Scottish crags and spend the winter in North Africa.

The two dotterel on the Norfolk coast, probably blown off course by the strong winds down the North Sea, were first seen by a party of Midlands birdwatchers on Sunday afternoon. The pair were rummaging with other migrants for insects on the grassy half of Gravelpit Hill.

Within an hour more than 100 orni-thologists were crowding around a field gate

The male dotterel is duller than his mate and incubates the eggs.

from which the migrants could be seen even without binoculars.

Cars parked at Salthouse Heath nearby caused traffic jams until light faded. Parties of ornithologists, visiting Cley and Salthouse, were queuing before dawn yesterday to see whether the dotterel had remained on the hill during the night.

Throughout the day the birds, tame by nature, wandered within yards of the road, slept in the furrows of the ploughed part of the field watched by an ever-increasing crowd of holidaymakers some of whom, without field glasses, were offering to buy binoculars from other watchers so that they could see the birds in detail.

It is expected that the birds will fly on towards Scotland within the next two days.

One motorist said that he had driven from Edgbaston, on the other side of Birmingham, during the night to see the birds. ''I don't want people to think I've been wasting petrol, but after 40 years of birdwatching I've never been able to see dotterel. By the way they are vanishing, I might never again.''

Dotterel are richly coloured, ash brown and chestnut with black heads and white bands extending backwards from their eyes around their napes.'

The breeding population has now fallen to about 100 pairs but there may be some sign of an expansion of the breeding range into the northern Pennines. Let us hope that the dotterel and also the twenty or fifty pairs of snow buntings which still breed in the Scottish Highlands will be able to survive. They will only do so if we preserve the habitat, and this must be possible since we have been preserving the grouse moors for more than a century.

Birds of moorlands and upland plantations

Three of Highland Scotland's major industries are deer stalking, grouse shooting and forestry and so man has a commercial interest in maintaining something near the status quo on the moorlands. It is appropriate, therefore, that the red grouse is described here as well as potential predators such as the merlin and the hen harrier. Grouse also occur in the Pennines and golden plover, lapwings, ring ouzel and twite often share this vulnerable habitat. On the open moors the magnificent short-eared owl also occurs and where the areas are planted with conifers the long-eared owl may also eventually find a niche.

Red grouse.

Red grouse *Lagopus lagopus*

The red grouse occupies the zone immediately below that occupied by the ptarmigan and thus avoids competition with it. At one time the red grouse was thought to be the only species of bird unique to Britain but the 40 centimetre (16 inch) plump-bodied creature is now said to be only a subspecies of the Arctic white-winged willow grouse, which occurs not only in Europe and Asia but also in North America. Recent work in Norway has successfully explained an aspect of willow grouse behaviour which has long mystified experts studying the bird throughout its range. A grouse sitting tight upon its eggs is often totally ignored by dogs even when they step right over it. It has been found that the bird, with a normal pulse-rate of about 150 per minute, can reduce this to almost 20 and can virtually stop breathing for a limited period. This suppresses the scent and the dogs do not detect the bird. If the bird wishes to fly then the pulse-rate can be rocketed to over 600 in less than a minute. The wonders do not stop there for it has also been shown that when her eggs are cooling the hen accelerates her heart-rate, and thus directs more blood into the area of bare skin called the brood patch which is pressed against the eggs. It is tempting to think that this control over the heart-rate might be useful for birds buried in snow and could also apply to the ptarmigan. Research is needed on other species; it may well be that 'temporary hibernation' is a regular facet of bird behaviour.

The grouse feeds mainly on heather shoots and many moors famous for their large bags of birds on the glorious twelfth of August are farmed to produce the most succulent heather. This is done by a regular burning of strips of heather to produce a moor which looks like a mosaic, with areas of dense nesting habitat interspersed with more open feeding areas. The six to fifteen eggs are laid in a scantily lined hollow scraped by the female and watched over by the slightly larger male, with his characteristic 'go back' call, for a period of about 26 days. The young are very vulnerable, but feed on insects, which are richer in protein than seeds. They can usually fly within a fortnight. It is important that they fly as soon as possible since predators, including stoats and weasels, have hungry young to feed – as do such birds as the merlin and the hen harrier.

Merlin *Falco columbarius*

If one examines the fortunes of Britain's birds of prey in recent years all show increases with one exception – the merlin, whose breeding population has probably plunged below 400 pairs (although it is a difficult bird to census). The large conspicuous birds of prey such as the eagle, buzzard and peregrine are easy to spot and count, whilst the hovering kestrel presents no problem to the censusing bird watcher. The merlin, on the other hand, is a small bird with a swift, low but ever so deadly flight. Their hunting efficiency makes merlins the enemy of the gamekeeper, but a study of its diet shows clearly that birds such as the meadow pipit, ring ouzel, skylark and twite have most to fear. The male is a small bird of about 25 centimetres (10 inches) with upper parts of slate-blue and the nape and dorsal surface of finely toned light brown, often heavily streaked. The female can be 33 centimetres (just over 13 inches) and has a shorter tail than her mate, whilst the upper surface is a much darker brown and the under surface is lighter, making the contrast between back and belly more clearly marked. Merlins tend to spend the winter on the coast, returning to the hills to breed during April. It is usually May before the nest in the heather contains a clutch of around four blotched purplish-brown eggs. Both sexes incubate for about 30 days, but once the young are hatched the male catches the food and brings it to the female who feeds the young. The late laying is obviously geared to coincide with a glut of young meadow pipits and skylarks that are easy to catch and provide a food supply which enables merlins to fledge in just under a month. It is almost certain that the decline of the merlin is due to loss of suitable habitat, perhaps accelerated by human disturbance. The RSPB have recently initiated an experi-

Opposite
Merlins are increasingly threatened by egg collectors and unscrupulous falconers who steal their chicks.

ment on Welsh merlins in which small radio transmitters are attached to the tail feathers of adults. They can be tracked and their preferred habitats mapped.

Hen harrier *Circus cyaneus*

This bird has long been regarded as the greatest threat to grouse moors and unenlightened landowners still often encourage their gamekeepers to set poletraps, even though illegal, to kill the magnificent bird. A common bird before the advent of the grouse moor, the hen harrier declined almost to extinction. Lowland heaths, where once it hunted in freedom, disappeared and there was no sanctuary even on the uplands. Only in the far north in Orkney and beyond in the highlands of Norway did the hen harrier retain its population and it is from these remote spots that the species has made its comeback. The population on mainland Britain is now approaching 800 pairs. As is the case with all the harriers, sexual dimorphism is pro-

nounced. The blue-grey male has a very clear white rump – a feature which distinguishes him from Montagu's harrier (*Circus pygargus*). The size is about 50 centimetres (20 inches) or perhaps a little smaller. The female has a white rump, and also has a series of rings on her tail. Indeed, the difference between the sexes is so profound that at one time they were thought to be separate species, the female being known as the ring-tailed hawk and the male as the hen harrier, presumably because of his occasional forays into the poultry pen. The diet consists mainly of birds and mammals which are taken by surprise on the ground due to the slow, almost silent flight and the harrier's ability to hover and, if the wind is right, to edge slightly backwards until over the prey. The nest is inevitably a hollow on the ground and from three to six light bluish eggs very occasionally with reddish markings are laid during May. The bulk of the nest construction is the work of the female and she incubates the eggs for the

whole of the 30-day incubation period. During this time she is called away periodically by the male for food, which is passed to her in the air either from foot to foot or by a wonderfully co-ordinated drop-and-catch technique. The young do not fly until their sixth week but the parents continue to care for them until they are more than two months old. As we saw with the eagle, incubation begins with the first egg thus producing young of various sizes and strengths. In really adverse conditions the elder eat the younger and at least some of the clutch survive. In human terms this appears cruel, but nature has no time for sentiment – only survival of the species matters.

Sometimes moorland ornithologists can become mesmerised by grouse and their enemies, or supposed enemies, but moorland is also the habitat of other delightfully attractive species, including the golden plover and the green plover, or lapwing.

Golden plover *Pluvialis apricarius*
To me the golden plover, with its plaintive whistling call, epitomises the springtime

moorlands. About 30,000 pairs now breed in Britain, mainly concentrated in northern England and Scotland, since the 'goldie', unlike the lapwing, finds lowland breeding sites totally unsuitable. It has, however, apparently found a method of dealing successfully with potentially overcrowded breeding sites. Working in north-east Scotland, Raymond Parr ('Sequential breeding by Golden Plovers', *British Birds*, vol. 72, pp. 499–503) found that each breeding pair occupied and defended a nesting area in which the clutch of three or four mottled eggs was laid in mid-April and after about a month's incubation by both sexes the young hatched and left the nest within hours. When they can fly in about a month they join the adult flocks. In his study area Parr noted a number of apparently non-breeding adults, but he eventually realised that they were waiting for the resident pair to raise their single brood before moving into the successful site and breeding themselves. If this is reflected in other areas it could well double the breeding habitat, but despite this the population of this attractive round-headed 28 centimetre (11½ inch) plover is decreasing.

Opposite
The hen harrier is now making a dramatic
comeback in Britain.

The golden plover — one of the loveliest birds of
upland Britain.

An alert lapwing looking for earthworms.

Green plover or lapwing

Vanellus vanellus

Numbers of this bird are also falling but, with a breeding population of some 200,000 pairs, it is still our most common plover and the wheeling winter flocks over farm and estuary remain a feature of the British countryside. Likewise in spring the moors echo to their pee-wit call, and their beating wings during the display flight show clearly why they were originally given the name of 'flapwing' which has only recently been shortened to lapwing. Its scientific name derives from the Latin word for a fan, again referring to the noise of the vibrating wings. Lapwings, like the moorhen, seem able to anticipate changes in the weather. Some British birds move south for the winter, and are replaced by wintering Scandinavian birds, whilst others drop down to the coast unless really heavy weather is coming, when they move westwards, often into Ireland – there is even the occasional record of a British lapwing turning up in North America.

A recent survey has revealed a worrying situation with regard to the breeding population of lapwings, although in winter:

'Many thousands of wintering Lapwings can be seen feeding and roosting in low-lying fields. The strongest concentrations occur in the Midlands where huge flocks, some well over 6,000, are recorded.

These winter populations paint a seemingly healthy picture for the Lapwing in this country, but the facts prove otherwise.

The birds we see in winter have moved south and west into Britain from Scandinavia and Central Europe immediately following their breeding season. Our own breeding Lapwings meanwhile have moved south to warmer climes on the continent.

Over the past 20 years there has been a major decline in the numbers of Lapwings breeding in southern Britain. This fact has come to light through the Common Birds Census, a survey organised by the British Trust for Ornithology. Since its inception in 1961 the CBC (to give it its more familiar title) has monitored bird populations in selected habitats, especially farmland and woodland.

Results show that in counties where the amount of pasture has been halved, and converted to cereals, there has been a fivefold reduction in the numbers of breeding Lapwings.

Information from another BTO monitoring survey, the Nest Record Scheme, confirms the decline. Nest record figures suggest a great decrease in the proportion of eggs hatching. Between 1960 and 1980 the percentage of successfully hatched eggs fell from 75% to just under 20% in areas where there was a gradual but increasing switch from grassland to arable farming.'

Breeding lapwings are usually back on the hilly breeding grounds by March and eggs are being laid from April onwards, when several pairs breed in close proximity. The nest is usually sited on a tuft of grass in a damp field and the clutch size is of four olive-brown,

darkly blotched eggs, which both sexes incubate for about a month. The young fledge in about 40 days, but the female takes most of the responsibility for protecting the young, often producing an impressive distraction display to lure away clumsy sheep or cattle and also more determined predators, which imagine that a bird with a broken leg or wing is easy prey. There is little difference between the sexes of this 30 centimetre (12 inch) black-and-white crested plover. A close look will show that the black portions of the plumage have a greenish tinge and there is a distinctive orange colour under the rump. Some workers are of the opinion that the male shows a clearer distinction between the dark and light areas and they also state that on average the crest is 30% longer in the male.

Ring ouzel *Turdus torquatus*

The ring ouzel, as its scientific name implies, is a member of the thrush family. In fact, the blackbird was once known as the common ouzel. The male blackbird is black but his mate is brown – a sexual distinction which also holds good for the ring ouzel. The male ring ouzel has a ring or rather a crescent of white around the throat, which is almost absent in the female. This 25 centimetre (10 inch) migrant returns to the Highlands in March from North Africa and southern Europe and the pair build their grass-based nest in a bank among the heather. Competition with the more aggressive blackbird is avoided by habitat preference, few blackbirds choosing to nest above the tree line, whilst very few of the 10,000–16,000 pairs of British ring ouzels choose to nest below it. Once the pair has established territory, from three to six greenish-white eggs flecked with brown are laid. Both birds assist in the incubation, which lasts 12–14 days, and the feeding of the young, which fly at 15 days. In order to produce two clutches the male often takes charge of the first brood of youngsters while the female incubates the second clutch. In this way the second crop of youngsters is ready to begin the return migration during late August or September, although some birds remain into October.

The wild moors which are the summer

The ring ouzel – an upland thrush.

of the ring ouzel are also favoured by the meadow pipit, and by one of the most interesting small brown birds found in Britain, the twite.

Twite *Acanthis flavirostris*

The twite is thought by many workers to be a true upland finch which had its origins in the highlands of Tibet and spread into Europe during the Ice Ages. As the highlands of Britain have become warmer the twite's range has diminished until just a few areas of Scotland, the Pennines of Lancashire and the hills of Lakeland provide a habitat cool enough for a population now thought to number between 20,000 and 40,000 breeding pairs. The twite also shows an unusual form of territorial behaviour, since the male is not interested in a fixed geographical territory but prefers to defend the area around his chosen female. This is a sensible arrangement as it allows the female the space to feed without being worried by the lecherous attentions of more than one male. She can thus build up her body reserves so that two broods of eggs can be developed within her. The nests are very often built in loose colonies among heather or low bushes such as gorse, but are usually less than 2 metres (6 feet) from the ground, and often on the ground itself. Five or six deep-blue eggs marked with brown are laid and incubated by the female, protected by the male, for just under a fortnight. The young are fed from the throat by both sexes and are able to fly on or about the fifteenth day after hatching.

Twites are often overlooked because of their rather nondescript brownish appearance. Somewhat darker than a linnet, in winter the twite can be distinguished by its yellowish bill, which changes to a greyish colour in the breeding season. The lores and throat of the twite are orange-buff-coloured and the male has a distinct rosy-pink rump. In the main the twite is a seed eater but it is quite able to switch to a protein diet when insects are available during the summer months. Just as with the ring ouzel and the blackbird we find the twite separated from the linnet by the two having different breeding niches determined by altitude, and the twite has often been referred to as the mountain linnet.

When we come to compare the distribution of the short-eared with the long-eared owl we find a vegetational differentiation. The former species breeds on open moorlands, but if these are planted with conifers there is obviously a change of all wildlife, including birds, and the short-eared owl is replaced by its long-eared cousin. It should be stressed that the 'ears' are not real ears, but tufts of feathers concerned with display. They have nothing to do with hearing.

Short-eared owl *Asio flammeus*
The short-eared owl is probably the more common of the two with a breeding population estimated to be between 1,000 and

A short-eared owl – breeds on the moors and winters on the coast.

10,000 pairs. This is a wide range and probably reflects the difficulty in censusing these upland birds. The breeding population of the long-eared owl (*Asio otus*) is thought to be about 3,000 pairs, but the population of both species is swelled during the winter by immigrants from northern Europe. The short-eared is quite a large owl, measuring some 38 centimetres (15 inches), and is frequently seen hunting by daylight when its short tail and the slow deliberate gliding strokes of its broad wings plus the absence of the white rump distinguish it from the hen harrier. The fact that the owl hunts at a different time (early morning and late afternoon) plus the fact that it generally prefers small mammals to birds prevents serious competition between the two moorland-based predators. This owl can also often be distinguished from other owls by the fact that it perches horizontally rather than in an upright posture like a sitting cat.

The birds are on the breeding grounds by March and the display flight is impressive and, for an owl, very delicate, until concluded by a tumbling twisting fall accompanied by a 'boo-boo-boo' call. The nest is a mere scrape in the heather and between four and eight eggs are usually laid, although in years when short-tailed field voles are numerous the clutch size may reach twelve or even thirteen and two broods may be raised instead of the usual one. The female takes responsibility for the incubation period of about a month but during this time she is provided with food by the male, who also fiercely protects her against predators, including man. The young can fly within a month of hatching and by the end of August the uplands are deserted in favour of coastal areas or lowland heaths.

Birds of lowland heaths

As we have seen thoughout this book all habitats are under some degree of threat but the lowland heaths are especially vulnerable, particularly during long hot summers. 1976 was just such a summer and its effect was graphically described by Colin Bibby in the *BTO News* of October 1976:

'After a dry summer in 1975, and a dry winter following, heathland enthusiasts were more than usually apprehensive about the fire hazard this spring. Accidental fires are most common in spring before the vegetation growth starts and during the re-emergence of human visitors (grockles). As feared, this spring was bad, but worse was to come with the arid summer leaving parched heaths even more inflammable. By July, smoke and the clamour of fire engines were a constant feature of life. Continual heathland fires joined Ulster and the economy as daily features of news. The Dartford Warbler was even mentioned on the front page of *The Times* (a first?).

At last as I write in mid-September it is raining and the crowds have gone home. The time to take stock has come. Enormous areas of Surrey, amongst them Thursley nature reserve, are blackened wastes, though the New Forest has fared less badly. In Dorset we have lost three of the seven best areas including Hartland Moor National Nature Reserve; about a fifth of the county's Dartford Warblers have been dispossessed. The loss of Hartland Moor was especially sad to me as I had been conducting a weekly mapping census for the previous two years and knew most of the colour-ringed Dartford Warblers personally. On Friday 13th August I made my last visit with binoculars; over the following three days, the fire-beater was the instrument for the job in a near hopeless attempt to save at least something. Now my studies on the Dartford Warbler are prematurely ended.

What have we lost? Birds are better equipped for immediate survival than many other creatures though some active nests including such rarities as the Hobby were destroyed. We watched one Nightjar in a futile injury-feigning display right beside the flames. No doubt there were eggs or young but we couldn't find them. Some adult birds probably perished but I watched Dartford Warblers fluttering through smouldering stems after a holocaust so severe that one fire-fighter was overcome and had to be taken to hospital. One ringed adult was still in its territory a week later though no vegetation remained: it seems that just as in severe

Dartford warblers are threatened by loss of
habitat and heathland fires.

winters, this bird is not accustomed to going elsewhere in response to bad times. More important than loss of individual birds is the fact that a fire renders a heath unsuitable for some years so the overall holding capacity for the rarer species is reduced.

In the longer term of course the sites will recover and the birds will return. Woodlarks and Stonechats are early colonists after fire. Meadow Pipits will be back within a couple of years but it will be 6–8 years before the fauna is completed by the return of Dartford Warblers. More worrying is the effect fires have in encouraging the spread of bracken and birch which, especially in Surrey, will destroy the heaths unless actively resisted. The extreme drought of this summer resulted in very hot fires which burnt root-stocks and consumed the litter layers which harbour seeds. Regeneration of heather will be delayed some time in places.

The damage to reptiles, especially the very rare Smooth Snake and Sand Lizard, has been severe. Many individuals survive the flames by burrowing but later they find nothing to eat and in turn are snapped up by scavenging gulls, corvids and raptors which move in after a fire. Local populations will have been eliminated and unless there is an adjacent source of new colonists, they will remain extinct. There have been great series of fires before, notably during the war, but heathland sites are now so fragmented and isolated that recolonisation of reptiles is ever less likely and they are losing strength by attrition.'

The sad declines reported here have continued especially during the hot summer of 1983 and the population of the Dartford warbler is now below 200 pairs, that of the nightjar below 5,000 pairs and the red-backed shrike, once reasonably common in Britain, has now been reduced to below 500 breeding pairs.

Dartford warbler *Sylvia undata*

The Dartford warbler is only 12·5 centimetres (5 inches) long and spends a great deal of its time skulking in vegetation, but when in view its dark coloration and long tail typify the species. The cock is dark brown on the upper parts but the head is slate-grey and the underparts a dull wine-colour. Both the female and the juvenile are paler. The nest is usually sited in heather or gorse and although the male builds a few 'cock nests' of his own the female prefers to build her own from grass, lining it with roots and feathers. Three or four dirty-white eggs are laid in late April or early May and are incubated by the hen for just under a fortnight. Both sexes feed the young, which can fly before they are two weeks old, thus giving ample time for two or three broods to be raised. The diet consists mainly of insects and spiders and this accounts for the problems faced by Dartford warblers during tough winters.

Nightjar *Caprimulgus europaeus*

This summer visitor was once referred to by countryfolk as the 'fern owl' but it can be distinguished from all other night-flying birds by its smooth, twisting and silent flight, long wings and tail. The huge eyes enable it to see well in dim light and the small bill can be opened into a huge gape which has a sticky interior making it function like a mobile fly-paper. The male can be distinguished from his mate and from young birds by the presence of white spots on his primary feathers; the outer tail feathers are tipped with white. The 26 centimetre (10½ inch) species is well camouflaged and is difficult to see but its presence is usually indicated by its loud churring notes, which seem to carry for miles. The favoured habitat is on the edge of woodland close to moors.

The clutch of two eggs is usually laid in a scrape on the ground and incubated by both sexes for about 18 days, the young flying after another 18 days following feeding by both parents, which bring insects caught on the wing. There is usually enough time for a pair to raise two broods.

Nightjars arrive in Britain from Africa during late April and May and leave by September. In recent years nightjars have declined – partly due to weather changes, though this is probably not the main reason. Dartford warblers and nightjars are species which have suffered not because we have failed to try to protect the birds but because we have failed to realise the importance of habitat. For an investor land is the most sensible asset to hold, and speculators have ruined the heathland areas of the southern counties and have now turned their sinister attentions to the farming land of Britain. Some of the many problems here will be discussed in Chapter 8.

Opposite
The nightjar is facing extinction in Britain because of loss of habitat.

8 Farmlands

Modern farmland occupies about 80% of Britain's land surface despite the fact that only 2–3% of the country's workforce is employed upon it. The high degree of mechanisation must therefore profoundly affect the wildlife which lives upon it and we must also remember that this area includes the rivers, ponds, hedges, copses and bogs which often lie within the boundaries of farms. Farming practices will obviously vary according to the type of soil and these in turn will have just as much if not more affect upon the wildlife than

The buzzard – recovering after centuries of persecution.

the climate. The dry flat lands of East Anglia have proven ideal for growing grain. Here hedges have been found to restrict movement of machinery and have been grubbed up without thought being given to the value of a hedge as a windbreak. Soil has eroded and birds of the hedgerow have disappeared. Herbicides and pesticides have also been used as a short-term solution rather than with forethought, and many birds perished along with thousands of colourful wild flowers and the insects which depended upon them. The Fenland loams have proven ideal for growing vegetables – another very mechanised and cost-conscious industry which always spells danger to wildlife. On the hill farms sheep were thought to lose lambs to predators such as eagles, buzzards, peregrines and other birds with hooked bills and talons. Without any proof whatever the wholesale slaughter of these species was embarked upon. Finally, in south-western England the rich pasturelands have survived to provide sustenance for pedigree dairy and beef cattle and it is in these areas that wildlife has fared comparatively well.

We often assume that we lost our woodlands to provide timber for household and industrial fuel, houses and furniture. The shipbuilding industry accelerated as we became more and more industrialised and dependent upon imports and exports. Forest clearances were planned from the earliest years of human civilisation and the word 'field' derives directly from the Old English word *feld*, which simply meant an area in which the trees had been felled. Thus in early days fields were cut from the forest and this must have been of great benefit to many birds, most of which preferred the woodland edge where light could penetrate rather than the dark cold interior. Gradually the fields became more numerous and the woodland less and less dense until only hedges were left, which the wildlife gratefully used as cover. Thus in this chapter on the bird life of farmland we will consider the birds of the hedgerows, birds of the fields, and finally the birds of the farm buildings themselves.

Birds of the hedgerow

Cricket at Lord's, cucumber sandwiches, tennis at Wimbledon, tea at four and hedges are typical of old England, but if you ask a dozen people to define a hedge you will be given a dozen different answers. As we have seen, the original hedges may have been the remnants of the ancient woodland, but gradually they were used to mark the boundaries of land, especially from 1603 onwards when the first Enclosure Act was passed – the last being pushed through Parliament just 300 years later. One bird typical of the hedge is the so-called hedge sparrow which breeds and feeds within the area, but the partridge uses the hedge as a shelter bed, the rook merely for breeding, while the introduced little owl has found a stone-wall 'hedge' to be an ideal niche.

Hedge sparrow *Prunella modularis*

The hedge sparrow is not very accurately named and a superficial glance at the narrow bill suitable for taking insects will separate it from the tough seed-crushing bill of the sparrow family. It is far more accurately named the dunnock. Hedges provide a fantastic variety of food items – grass seed for linnets, hawthorn berries for fieldfares and redwings, rosehips and rowan berries for mistle thrushes and wintering waxwing, caterpillars for tits, ash keys for chaffinches, snails for song thrushes, rodents for owls, and all the smaller birds are fair game for the sparrow-hawk. None of these species, however, lives totally within the hedge as does the secretive 15 centimetre (6 inch) dunnock, whose presence is seldom noticed unless the tuned ear listens for the thin 'peep-peep-peep' contact call.

John Ray in 1678 called the species the *Curruca* and noted that it 'lays sea green or pale blue eggs which neatly emptied and wired I have seen fair ladies wear on their ears as pendants'. It is known that dunnocks, which belong to the accentor family, were present in the woodlands, doubtless feeding and breeding in the shrub layer, and its old name was the sugge, which is thought to have given rise to the place-names of Sugham in

Dunnock at nest – one of our shyest birds and therefore difficult to census.

Surrey, Sugworth in Lancashire and Sugworthy in Devon. The species is a favourite victim of the cuckoo and I enjoy the account of this written by the great naturalist the Reverend Gilbert White. I can see a twinkle in his eye as I read:

'You wonder, with good reason, that the hedge sparrow can be induced at all to set upon the egg of a cuckoo without being scandalised at the vast disproportioned size of the suppositious egg; but the brute creation, I suppose, have very little idea of size, colour and number.'

Recent work suggests a more simple explanation, namely that given a choice between a large object and a small object the larger is chosen. Biologists call this responding to a supernormal stimulus. Doubtless we can all

cite examples from human activities, especially in the world of commerce. Is this not just sheer greediness?

The dunnock is a secretive bird and there is also some seasonal movement in and out of the country. These factors make the dunnock difficult to census but the breeding population is probably in excess of 5 million pairs, though there must have been some decline as hedges have been lost in some areas. The breeding season begins in April in a nest built by the hen only from twigs lined with dead leaves and completed by a circle of moss. The hen also takes charge of the 13-day incubation period although the male stays close at hand and helps to feed the young, which can fly before they are a fortnight old. There is thus ample time to raise two and often three broods.

Partridge *Perdrix perdrix*
The partridge was formerly known as the common partridge but is now called the grey partridge. It is found at its highest density in

small fields separated from their neighbours by substantial hedges. The species has long been popular with shooting men and it was they who introduced the red-legged or French partridge (*Alectoris rufa*) into the English countryside to add a little more variety to their 'sport'. The distinction between the two species is easily made. Both species show a reddish tail in flight, but a look at a bird on the ground will reveal that the 'Frenchie' has white cheeks and throat with a conspicuous black border and the flanks are also liberally provided with bars of black, white and chestnut-red. The legs and bill of the French partridge are red, and by contrast the grey partridge is a rounder, rather smaller bird of 30 centimetres (12 inches) with a brownish head and no white cheeks; the neck and underparts are grey. The flanks are barred with chestnut and white and in all males and most females there is a chestnut-coloured patch on the breast shaped like a horseshoe. There seems to be a tendency for older females to lose this patch although this does not seem to have been statistically proved.

The main habitat requirement of the grey partridge is rough cover which provides it with seeds for food and good nest sites. For this reason it has declined in south-eastern England, but there are still about 500,000 breeding pairs widely spread throughout Britain. There can be no doubt that the use of pesticides in many areas, as well as loss of habitat, earlier ploughing, and recent climatic changes with cooler and – more important – wetter springs have all adversely affected the population. A single clutch of between eight and twenty-three shiny brown eggs is laid in a scrape on the ground sheltered by herbage. The eggs are incubated by the female alone for 24 days. Once the young have hatched it is a full-time job for both parents to look after their scuttling offspring until they can fly, often at the very early age of 11 days, although some less precocious are not airborne until the sixteenth day. The partridge – unlike its smaller, 18 centimetre (7½ inch) and fast-declining relative the quail (only about 300 pairs now breed) – is a resident breed in Britain's farmlands.

Rook *Corvus frugilegus*

The rook has probably always been a colonial nester, preferring the woodland edge; it has certainly benefited more than most other species from the creation of hedges and fields. The hedge provides the nest site (an elm is especially favoured) while a field full of worms and leatherjackets makes the perfect feeding ground. About 1½ million pairs now breed in Britain. They stay quite close to their natal rookery throughout the winter, but during this time – especially in really tough weather – their numbers are swelled by large numbers of continental immigrants. The effect of Dutch elm disease has been disastrous. Many traditional rookeries have been destroyed and the displaced birds are slowly adapting to other species of tree.

The vast majority of rookeries are sited on land below 130 metres (400 feet). During the winter the birds pay periodic visits to their nests, but territories are already being established by early March and the bulky nest of twigs is built by both sexes, who prefer very high sites among the thin branches. It would appear that the male selects the site and then solicits the female. The high sites are almost certainly to keep the eggs and young safe from climbing predators, but the choice has disadvantages if storm-force winds should whip through the area in April or May and blast away the fragile supporting branches. The female takes responsibility for incubation, which takes about 18 days, but the male feeds his mate and also takes an active part in feeding the young. These number from three to five, although occasional clutches of six or even seven are produced.

Adult rooks can be distinguished from the carrion crow (*Corvus corone*) by the bare greyish-white patch on the face, but before the young rooks develop this feature prior to breeding at the age of two the best distinguishing feature is that the flanks of the rook are feathered and those of the crow are naked. This gives the rook the appearance of having baggy trousers. Both species are the same size – 45 centimetres (18 inches) – but the crow is a heavier bird. No bird is hated more by the farmer than the scavenging carrion crow unless it be the magpie (*Pica*

pica), another member of the crow family. The rook, being a crow, is sometimes tarred with the same brush. Is this fair? I would say definitely that it is not. Like all crows it is omnivorous, but it is more partial to vegetable matter than most of the family and even its meat ration is mainly agriculturally harmful rodents and insects, and this more than counterbalances any ill effect the species may have on crops. This fact is appreciated more on the continent than in Britain and in some areas of Europe the rook is a protected species.

Little owl *Athene noctua*

The little owl is an example of the successful and deliberately planned introduction of a new species into Britain. The reason the project succeeded was that the favoured niche of the little owl was not taken by any other owl. The tawny owl occupies deciduous woodland, the long-eared coniferous plantations, the short-eared moorlands and the barn owl farm buildings – but the hedges, whether of vegetation or stone, were an unfilled niche. Lord Lilford released the

22 centimetre (8½ inch) liver-brown pale spotted and streaked little owl on his Northamptonshire estates around 1889 and since then it has been a success story of almost unparalleled proportions, the population now being between 7,500 and 16,000 pairs with just a few set-backs in areas using high levels of insecticide and herbicides. There was initially a natural fear that game birds such as the partridge would be taken by this round-winged species, which seems to prefer to hunt during daylight, but an analysis of its pellets seems to find the species innocent of almost all charges brought against it. Insects are taken, as are amphibians such as frogs, toads and newts, as well as small mammals. Small birds such as meadow pipits do appear on the diet but partridges hardly at all – if ever. For the most part little owls are resident, but in times of real hard weather some individuals may move from upland farm to the coast and it was

The hooded crow (a variety of carrion crow), like most of the crow family, can be a menace to farmers, especially in Scotland.

The little owl – introduced from Holland in the 1870s.

probably one of these which gave me one of my most unusual sightings, a report of which was published in *British Birds* (vol. 69, 1976, p. 272):

'On January 7th, 1975, at Walney Island, Cumbria I was watching a group of feeding dunlins (*Calidris alpina*) when suddenly a little owl (*Athene noctua*) emerged from behind a large tide stranded tree trunk. The owl flew low at the dunlins and seemed to strike at them with its talons, but caught nothing. I saw what I took to be the same bird repeat the

process on 9th January, again without success. On the morning of 11th January, however, I found the decapitated body of a turnstone (*Arenaria interpres*) beneath the tree trunk. On this evidence I surmise that the little owl was including small waders in its diet, although I failed to locate any pellets.'

The nest of the little owl is most often sited in hollow trees or holes in walls but there are records of buildings and even sea cliffs being used. If the holes are sufficiently large the bird may take its prey home and dismember it in peace. The single, occasionally double, clutch of between two and seven round white eggs is laid in late April or May and incubated only by the female for about a month. Both sexes feed the young, which can fly about 38 days after hatching.

Birds of the field

During the summers of 1981 and 1982 I wandered at will through the fields on the delightful Hebridean island of Canna, then still in the ownership of John Lorne Campbell, the well-known Gaelic scholar and eminent entomologist. He had never allowed artificial fertiliser or any herbicide, fungicide

The corncrake – still a common nesting species in the Hebrides, but sadly declined in mainland Britain.

or pesticide to be used on his land and the rich crops were harvested late in the year and by traditional methods. My walks were like journeys backwards through time into the fields of bygone Britain, abounding with hosts of flowers including lesser butterfly and marsh orchids, kidney vetch, red bartsia, hemp nettle, wild comfrey, and grass of parnassus. In England such 'weeds' as these have long since been sprayed into oblivion by the use of herbicides and early harvesting to allow for two crops of grass and increased profits. Birds such as the summer-visiting wheatears, with their white rumps flashing in the sun, have been reduced. So also have cuckoos, meadow pipits and skylarks, but it is the corncrake which has suffered most. Canna is one of its last refuges and as I wandered its fields on a gentle Hebridean evening the sound of the reeling bird issued from every field much as it must have done in the fields of ancient Britain.

Corncrake *Crex crex*

The corncrake is 27 centimetres (11 inches) long. Its scientific name obviously derives from the monotonous sound made by the territorially ambitious males, but it is also known as the land rail. Once common in Britain, there are now less than 600 pairs but there is a higher population, possibly as many as 5,000 pairs, in Ireland. Quite the reverse of the Victorian child, the corncrake is more often heard than seen, but it is occasionally seen in flight when its long legs dangle below the body. It is rather surprising to find that a bird which appears to fly so badly is a summer visitor which has its winter home in the southern half of Africa – no mean journey. The nest is sited on the ground but hidden deep in long grass and like the bird itself difficult to find. It is usually the female which incubates the clutch of from six to fourteen eggs for just over a fortnight. Almost immediately they are dry the young move around and can soon fend for themselves, although they cannot usually fly until well into their eighth week. The diet is varied but ideal for a field-based species – seeds and grasses are both eaten along with snails, slugs, worms and spiders, mostly taken very early in the morning or just before dark as the corncrake is crepuscular in its habits.

Cuckoo *Cuculus canorus*

In 'the good old days' the cuckoo shared its habitat with the corncrake. It has also declined significantly in recent years but the British breeding population is still around 10,000 breeding pairs. The cuckoo must have had more words written about it than any other British species and yet we still know relatively little about its behaviour. The bird measures about 34 centimetres (13 inches); it has blue-grey upper-parts and breast, the rest of the under surface is darkly barred, and the long tail is very distinctive, particularly in flight. The sexes are alike and bear a superficial resemblance to a sparrow-hawk which no doubt accounts for the old-fashioned belief that cuckoos changed into sparrow-hawks for the winter. To the parochial British prior to the eighteenth century this theory of transmutation of species was more acceptable than the idea of migration. The insect-eating bill of the cuckoo, the well-known onomatopoeic call of the male and the babbling sound of the female are all easy points of distinction.

Once mated and her eggs fertilised, the hen must set about finding a host to incubate her eggs and raise the chicks. Each female produces from twelve to twenty-four eggs. These are laid one at a time in individual nests and cuckoo eggs have been found in the nests of over 100 different songbirds, including that of the little goldcrest – how this was insinuated into the nest remains a mystery, or should I say a miracle! There is evidence to suggest that an individual female tends to produce eggs each with her own characteristics and that she positively selects a host to match these eggs. There may well turn out to be different subspecies of the European cuckoo, each specialising in a particular host species. Once more work has been done, or perhaps as evolution continues with the passage of time, we shall have meadow-pipit cuckoos, reed-warbler cuckoos and pied-wagtail cuckoos. All these host birds are considerably smaller than the cuckoo and this means that the nest parasite must produce very small eggs which weigh only 3% of the body weight, whereas the eggs of its host are about 10% of the female's body weight. Likewise the incubation time for a cuckoo's egg is only 12 days so that the young bird hatches before those of the fosterer and the young cuckoo can remove all opposition by arching its back and tipping its host's eggs over the nest rim. Bringing such a complex breeding sequence to a successful conclusion involves careful planning and it has been shown that the hen cuckoo watches the suitable local nests carefully and then moves in quickly, lays her own egg in the nest, and removes one of the host's clutch. She always chooses an incomplete clutch to be certain that incubation has not yet begun and that her own egg will be the first to hatch. She then either eats the egg she has removed or carries it away and drops it.

Thus the cuckoo has mapped out for itself a niche which has no competitor. It is also able to tap a unique feeding niche. Cuckoos feast greedily upon hairy and evil-tasting cater-

Young cuckoo.

pillars such as the emperor moth with which the digestive systems of other species appear unable to cope. In addition to such prickly customers cuckoos also eat centipedes, spiders and worms, but obviously the young feed readily on whatever food their foster parents may bring them.

Cuckoos are seldom heard in this country before April and the adults have usually departed for Africa before the end of August, the young following on about a month later. How they find their way is, as yet, a mystery. As they never come in contact with their parents the directions must be locked up within the egg and thus to call it genetic memory is a true statement, even though we cannot explain it. By the time it is 23 days old the young cuckoo towers above its hardworking foster parents, its red gape proving an irresistible cavern – another example of what is called a supernormal stimulus.

I once observed an amusing incident when I was watching a pair of meadow pipits doing their best to satisfy the appetite of a young cuckoo almost ready for flying and standing on the edge of the nest screaming for food. A song thrush was flying back to its own nest of youngsters a few metres away, carrying a beakful of worms. When it saw the red gape of the cuckoo it flickered its wings and hovered – obviously in amazement. It landed and deposited the worms into the open bill and shook its feathers in some confusion before returning to whence it came. I'll swear that it deliberately selected a different route back to its nest to avoid a second confrontation!

No wonder the poor meadow pipits looked exhausted before the genetic memory of their uninvited guest took over and it set off for Africa.

Meadow pipit *Anthus pratensis*
There is no shortage of meadow pipits on the fields and open lands of Britain, although the species does not cope too well in areas which

are extensively cultivated. Over 3 million pairs occur on these islands along with the almost equally abundant skylark. The meadow pipit measures around 14·5 centimetres (nearly 6 inches) and is probably the most typical small bird of the upland fields which it shares with curlews, lapwings, snipe and redshank. Birds of prey such as the merlin and the hen harrier rely heavily on the meadow pipit for their sustenance, but despite their attentions the species still thrives. Indeed it is essential that predatory birds do not become too numerous and that the prey should always be more common than the predator itself – this is nature's balance.

The breeding season of the meadow pipit begins with a soaring song flight. This is not so well controlled as that of the skylark but very impressive for all that, and ends with a parachute drop on fluttering wings typical of the pipit family. The male seeking territory has no need of a song post with such aerobatic skills at his disposal and the breeding season extends from March to as late as September,

during which time two, three and very occasionally four broods are reared. Small wonder the population holds steady despite the attention of predators! The nest is in a well hidden scrape in the ground or a bank and the normal clutch is of four or five and occasionally up to seven round, shiny and darkly mottled eggs. Most of the incubation, which lasts 14 days, is undertaken by the female, but the male joins in the chore of feeding the young.

Skylark *Alauda arvensis*
At 18 centimetres (7 inches) the skylark is larger than the meadow pipit and is widely spread throughout Britain. Its song has charmed romantic poets for centuries and is known to folk who neither know nor care what the bird looks like at close quarters. When, as is often the case, it is seen against a ploughed field the brownish streaked body with the paler underparts blends perfectly with the background. When a stiffish breeze is blowing the crest on the head can look quite

Meadow pipit.

Skylark feeding young.

substantial but the feathers are normally held flat. In flight the white edges of the tail and to a lesser extent on the hind margin of the wing are clearly seen and the undulating flight with fluttering wings is also typical. It is the male's wonderful soaring display flight, however, which typifies the species and which persuades the hen to construct her nest, often complete with a doorstep, in a tuft of grass. She lays a clutch of three or four eggs, which she incubates for the relatively short period of eleven days. The male joins in the feeding of the young, which leave the nest within ten days and flutter about for another ten before flying. The breeding period is in full swing by the end of April and this gives plenty of time for two and often three broods to be produced. Growing young are fed on worms and insects but adult skylarks are perfectly able to thrive on the seeds which abound in hedges and fields. Although the skylark has suffered in areas where poisonous chemicals are used there is no doubt that the species has benefited from human activities in creating fields from the ancient woodlands.

Birds of the farm buildings

The harvest period and times when stock are being fed in the farmyard may persuade

Fringilla coelebs to leave the beech woods and earn its vernacular name of chaffinch, while the crossbill will sometimes desert the conifers to raid the orchards. But neither of these species is regularly associated with farm buildings. In recent years prefabricated monstrosities have replaced old stone barns, and there is nothing that can be done to prevent this since farms are totally exempt from planning regulations. It would surely be far more economical on the taxpayer if grants were given to improve and repair old buildings with character rather than dole out larger sums on section-built structures which will last for years, not for centuries. The old buildings, with their beams and shuttered windows with the odd gap, served their purpose and offered a home to the useful barn owl and the attractive swallow. Orchards and gardens attract the beautiful goldfinch and greenfinch whilst the fruit trees are often stripped of buds by the far from welcome but nevertheless attractive bullfinch. In recent years most farms have had their resident collared doves, once rare but now approaching pest proportions in some areas.

Barn owl *Tyto alba*

The barn owl has long been recognised by farmers as their friend – a sort of cat with wings – and many of the old stone barns were built with a special owl window to allow the super rat-killer to enter and leave at will. Even the modern farmer with his new buildings is often prepared to encourage a guest by putting up specially designed nest boxes, though they do seem to be very effective. This may hopefully do something to increase the struggling population, which seems to have bottomed out at about 5,000 pairs although some estimates place the figure closer to 10,000. There are few more attractive species on the British list than the barn owl and some high-principled conservationists now collect barn owls injured by traffic and unable to fly, persuade them to breed in captivity, and release their healthy offspring into areas from which barn owls disappeared during less enlightened times.

During 1984 industry joined in an attempt to raise £10,000 to provide for research and the placing and monitoring of artificial nesting boxes for the barn owl. Commenting on the World Wildlife Fund's business sponsorship appeal for the 'Help a British Barn Owl Campaign', Sir Peter Scott, Chairman of the Fund's International Council, said: 'Conservation sponsorships can be of great benefit both to industry and to the environment in which we all live, and it is encouraging to see companies like Office Cleaning Services entering this field.' (OCS is the UK's largest privately owned group of companies in the field of office cleaning, building maintenance, industrial cleaning, etc.)

The hen barn owl normally lays her clutch of from four to seven round white eggs during late April on a heap of disgorged pellets but she never makes much of any pretence at nest building. The female begins to incubate as soon as the first egg is laid and so we find, in times of stress, the elder brethren eating their siblings if the parents are unable to maintain an acceptable supply of rodents and the occasional small bird. The fact that the young do not fledge for two or even three months means that only one clutch is usually reared, although there are occasional records of two at times when the rodent population is high.

Barn owls measure 34 centimetres (13½ inches) and have a very distinctive white plumage, which gives them a ghost-like appearance. Occasionally this is accentuated when birds roost in buildings where the beams are rotting. Pieces of wood become lodged under the feathers and there is a build-up of bioluminescent bacteria. When the barn owl is disturbed and stretches its wings a weird flashing light is produced – a spine-chilling experience even when you are expecting it. Goodness knows what effect it had upon the superstitious farm worker of old!

Swallow *Hirundo rustica*

The swallow, it would seem, has been associated with the human species for as long as we have existed, perhaps sharing the same cavern as the original cave man. Certainly man of the Pleistocene Period knew the swallow as its bones have been found with his artefacts and it was probably part of his diet. When man left

the caves and built houses it seems highly likely that the swallow moved with him and has been with him ever since. The present-day breeding population in Britain is probably between 500,000 and 1 million pairs but there has been a recent decline in population, though happily this is showing some signs of improvement. Good summers obviously help since all the swallow's food is taken on the wing and wet, windy weather affects both the adults and the young which they are trying to raise. The long curved wings and streaming outer tail feathers give this slender 19 centimetre (7½ inch) migrant greater power.

Swallows pour into Britain from South Africa during April and are ready to breed in May. The male bird returns to the same nest site year after year and if his mate has also survived she will rejoin him – a most remarkable feat of navigation. A new nest is

The barn owl is the farmer's friend and eats more rodents than the farm cat.

built on a ledge, porch or outhouse, or the one from last year repaired, both sexes working on the project and lining the nest with feathers. Once the four or perhaps five eggs, white but speckled with rusty-red, are laid the female does most of the incubating, which takes fourteen days, but both birds feed their young directly from the throat. Two broods are almost always raised and a third often attempted. This means that young swallows are often found in the nest as late as September, when most birds are feeding hard to build up their reserves prior to migration. Recent work has suggested that the earlier broods may assist in the feeding of the late broods, but even so these late birds may have less chance of surviving the migratory journey

Swallows in a Dorset barn.

The swallow lands on the ground only when collecting nesting material.

and those which do may not breed the following summer but need an extra year in which to mature.

Goldfinch *Carduelis carduelis*

The goldfinch is quite a small bird but it packs a great deal of vivid colour into its 12 centimetre (nearly 5 inch) frame, the top of the head being black and separated from the scarlet face by a white border. In flight the bright yellow patches flash in contrast with the black wings which have white terminal spots on the quills, and the white rump and dark tail can also be clearly seen. Such a beautiful bird was bound to attract the attentions of the old bird trappers as they had a ready sale of feathers to milliners, of live birds to cage-bird fanciers, and of dead ones to taxidermists. The Bird Protection Acts have certainly been a boon to goldfinches and as many as 300,000 pairs now breed in Britain. It is more numerous in the southern counties, but it is now increasingly common to see goldfinches feeding on the thistle seeds of the upland farm fields of Britain and for them to grace a farmyard with their presence. Although goldfinches are often defined as resident there is a westerly movement of a large proportion of birds, especially during spells of hard weather. In any event they are back in the breeding area before the end of March and the 'charms' of goldfinches, as the flocks are called, break up and look for nest sites. Fruit trees are favourite sites, and there is also a preference for the outermost twigs of branches. As the population increases and there is more pressure for space strange sites can be chosen. This is illustrated by one female which built her nest of roots, lichen and moss, lined with wool, in a disused gas lamp near a farm in a Yorkshire dale's village. Here she successfully raised her clutch of four eggs. This takes just under a fortnight and after being fed by both sexes the young fly in about 13 days, leaving ample time for two or even three broods to be raised.

Greenfinch *Chloris chloris*

When the greenfinch and bullfinch also occur in the area there is no competition for food and a look at the bill shapes will show why. The comparatively long and narrow bill of the goldfinch is ideal for extracting seeds from thistles and burdock. The greenfinch has a more powerful, broader bill which can handle larger, tougher seeds. Two million pairs breed in Britain and its nasal, 'zwee-ee-ee' call is known to most country folk and is now very much a sound associated with town parks.

Bullfinch *Pyrrhula pyrrhula*

Fortunately not so common as the greenfinch is the fruit farmer's enemy the bullfinch, of which over half a million pairs nest in Britain. The cock bird is very colourful indeed. The shiny black cap, wings and tail show up clearly against the rosy red undersurface. It can be easily identified in flight by its pure white rump. Compared with the male, the female is a dull bird, but if she is seen in the company of other birds without her mate her true beauty can be appreciated. The short stout bill is perfectly adapted for crushing seeds and berries, but unfortunately can also make short work of the succulent buds of fruit

A greenfinch on hawthorn.

trees. Farmers have tried trapping, shooting and an assortment of often bizarre bird scarers but the only sure way is to provide each tree with a protective net. There are also other birds around the farmyard which are far from welcome, one of the most remarkable being the collared dove.

Collared dove *Streptopelia decaocto*

The collared dove provides the ornithologist with the greatest unsolved mystery of the present day. This small dove (31 centimetres or 12½ inches) was confined to Turkey and the Balkans until 1930, when for no apparent reason, unless some genetic change took place, it began to expand its range. It was spotted in Lincolnshire in 1952 and three years later breeding was positively confirmed at Cromer in Norfolk. By 1964 the population had soared to 3,000 pairs and by 1970 was at the remarkable level of 25,000 pairs. By 1980 the population was 50,000 pairs with no sign of any slowing of the expansion. Competition with established pigeon species has been avoided by the collared dove carrying on its historically close connections with man at his workplace, for it readily took to granaries,

breweries, mills, warehouses and of course farm outbuildings. It has been so successful that in areas where it was once protected as a rare species it is now regarded as a serious pest. Part of the reason for the success of this pale grey-brown dove with a narrow black half-collar at the back of the neck is its protracted breeding season. Eggs have been reported in every month of the year but the peak period would seem to be around July. Two glossy white eggs are laid on a platform of twigs, usually in a tree but sometimes on a building. Both sexes incubate for about a fortnight, the male sitting by day and the female by night. Both parents feed the young directly from their crops, which produce pigeon milk, and the squabs, as the young are called, fly in just under three weeks. Two broods are regular but as many as five in a twelve-month period have been recorded. With such a breeding potential it is hardly surprising to find the spread continuing and the collared dove is rapidly becoming a bird of the town as well as of village and farm. In the towns, however, it is likely to face a much more frigid welcome from the street pigeon, which will be discussed in the next chapter.

9 Towns

Birds have always been part of man's towns from the days when the refuse of the streets was scavenged by the black kite and peregrines bred in the spire of Salisbury Cathedral. The pigeons were in central London long before Nelson's column was erected in Trafalgar Square. Modern cities are as attractive to birds as ever and three distinct habitats can be recognised. First there are the buildings themselves, which are used as roosts and nest sites by many species. Those which spring immediately to mind are the feral pigeon, house martin, swift, house sparrow, starling and kestrel. Any town or city will have its derelict areas – the open spaces of airports, railway sidings, and the disused

trappings of once thriving industries – and here are found the ubiquitous pied wagtail and the still quite rare but increasingly common black redstart and the little ringed plover. Finally there are the 'deliberate' open spaces of parks, cemeteries and the large gardens of the middle classes, all of which are to birds the equivalent of at least a hedge and in some cases a small wood. We must also remember that towns, with their houses and other buildings now so well heated, are warmer places and birds survive the long winter nights much better than they can ever do in the open countryside. It is also a fact that birds such as blackbirds, robins, thrushes and the like breed earlier in the town than in the country. This is due entirely to street lights which artificially lengthen the period of daylight. Day length is the factor which acts upon the hormones of birds and brings them into breeding condition. Thus the town-based naturalist may wish to escape into the fresh air of the countryside but must never forget that interesting birds are all around in even the busiest street of the city and each building will have its own avifauna – including St Paul's, The Tower of London or the mighty post office tower. One of the most varied of bird habitats is the grounds of Buckingham Palace.

Birds of buildings

Street pigeon *Columba livia*
No account of town birds could be considered adequate which did not take an in-depth look at the street pigeon, whose ancestor was the cliff-dwelling rock dove which made the natural transition from steep cliff to steep masonry with surprising ease. The 'pure' rock dove is some 31 centimetres (13 inches) long and has a white rump and two black bars

Female blackbird with young – blackbirds breed earlier in towns when street lights artificially increase the day length.

Domestic pigeons are descended from wild rock doves.

on the wing, whilst the upper surface is pale blue-grey and the undersurface off-white. Almost 100,000 pairs of rock doves still breed in the wild and show all of the characteristics described above but apart from in the Outer Hebridean islands and in Ireland interbreeding with racing pigeons and other domesticated forms has diluted some, if not all, of these characteristics and the pure wild bird is now hard to find.

Rock doves have a more rapid wingbeat than either wood pigeons or stock doves and are often mistaken for waders as they expertly ride the wind on approaching their nesting ledges in sea cliffs. It is no wonder that they find nesting on window-ledges an easy option. The population of the street pigeon is impossible to estimate since all railway stations, bridges, large buildings and open squares seem to be a mass of swirling wings and at times a 'hail of falling whitewash'.

Are pigeons in towns a health hazard? It would seem that they are: a fungus called *Cryptococcus neoformans* has been found in the droppings of feral pigeons which can not only attack human skin but can on occasions cause fatal damage to the lungs and nervous system. Psittacosis, a disease normally associated with parrots, can be transmitted to humans; it causes inflammation of the lungs and pneumonia. In 1944–5 a very worrying outbreak of the disease in Chicago was spread by pigeons and research found the virus responsible was present in the droppings plastered on public buildings. It has subsequently been found that over 60% of the Paris pigeons are carriers and that an even greater percentage of London and Manchester pigeons are affected. Another obvious vector is the starling which often takes over public buildings during the winter, but much healthier members of the

House martins are aerial acrobats.

Two young house martins communicating.

civic bird population are the house martin and the swift, both summer visitors.

House martin *Delichon urbica*
The house martin can easily be distinguished from the rest of the swallow family by its white feathered legs and rump whilst the forked tail of this 12·5 centimetre (5 inch) aerial acrobat is much shorter than the swallow's. Although they are common – the breeding population is thought to be between 300,000 and 600,000 – they are not so widely distributed as the swallow. Whilst single nests do occur, semicolonial breeding seems to

The swift – once known among country-folk as the 'devil bird'.

be preferred. Nests may be found in isolated farm buildings but house martins do penetrate much further into large towns and cities than do swallows and parts of London have thriving groups. Their diet is totally of insects caught on the wing but the martins fly higher than the swallows and thus direct competition between two species is once more avoided and the ecological niche theory survives intact. The nests are placed under the eaves of buildings and are made of mud carried on the bills of both sexes – quite a difficult task. Once the cup is complete the interior is lined with grass and feathers, and the sight of a colony busy building nests is a great joy for the urban bird watcher. During May or June, four or five pointed white eggs are laid, which both parents incubate for about a fortnight. This period is accepted by all workers, but

when we come to consider the fledging period of the house martin there is much more controversy. Witherby's *Handbook of British Birds* gives 19–22 days and Lind in 1960 gave a figure of 24 days. The latest opinion is that both parents feed the young for about 30 days and that the breeding season can go on well into September to allow the production of two or even three broods. There is also evidence to suggest that the young hang around the nest after they have fledged and may even help to feed subsequent broods, as in the case of young swallows. This is certainly not the case with the swift, which has its own unique and intriguing breeding cycle.

Swift *Apus apus*
The swift is not related to the swallows and martins but is more closely allied to the night-jars. It is, however, very much associated with buildings and parties of them twist in and out of houses, around and over rooftops

and earn their name of devil birds. Its stout 16 centimetre (6½ inch) dark sooty-brown – almost black – body, broken only by the white chin, long swept-back wings and short forked tail make it instantly recognisable. The swift arrives here in May and departs for its insect-rich African wintering grounds in August. The swift spends the majority of its time on the wing and out of the breeding season even roosts in flight. They actually mate in flight and 100,000 pairs breed in Britain. All of the insect food is taken in flight – the bill has a wide gape and a sticky interior similar to that of the nightjar – and the nesting material, such as feathers, is also collected on the wing. Indeed, if a swift is forced down its legs are so short that it cannot take off without struggling up an incline to provide early momentum. This is why the nests are sited in high buildings. They are made from a variety of material moulded together with the bird's saliva. The traditional bird's nest soup is made from the nest of an oriental relative of the European swift.

House sparrow feeding young.

A clutch of two or perhaps three pointed white eggs is incubated for about 20 days by both parents, which always roost together in the nest hole. Once the eggs have hatched the young take a long time to fledge – the precise time is very variable and is absolutely dependent upon the weather. Should a spell of cold wet weather prevent the parents from collecting sufficient food, the swiftlets are able to reduce their body temperature, blood pressure and heart-rate and enter into a limited period of suspended animation, which is to all intents and purposes a short period of hibernation. When suitable feeding weather returns the youngsters quickly raise the metabolic rate and get on with the urgent business of developing into adults in time to leave for Africa during August or early September. After the screaming devil birds have gone, life for the resident house sparrows and starlings must be a great deal quieter.

House sparrow *Passer domesticus*
The house sparrow is the best known and yet one of the least understood of the city birds. It is just under 15 centimetres (6 inches) long.

Tree sparrow at its nest hole.

Although difficult to census it has been estimated that between 4 and 7 million pairs breed in Britain, eggs having been found in each and every month of the year – no doubt due to the warmth and light of the city. Even so, the breeding period is at its peak between May and August with nest sites varying from niches in buildings to the high branches of trees, where the untidy straw nest is often confused with that of the less numerous (about 250,000 breeding pairs) and more woodland-bound 14 centimetre (5¾ inch) tree sparrow (*Passer montanus*). The male house sparrow can be distinguished by his grey crown – both the male and female tree sparrows have chestnut crowns and they also have a great deal more white on their cheeks. The black bib of the cock house sparrow is a lot less obvious in the winter and when the

birds are in the country the hen can be confused with the closely related bunting family, but she has no white on her tail and she does have a distinct pale stripe over her eye. Wherever man has settled and raised buildings the house sparrow has soon followed, except for a few remote island and highland farmsteads. They are efficient survivors and will eat almost anything, as can be clearly seen when the pugnacious creatures clear bird tables of all opposition.

Courtship is, like the rest of the sparrow lifestyle, anything but peaceful and a single female may be chased, and on occasions raped, by several males before she accepts one cock. She is then joined by her mate in the construction of the untidy but warm feather-lined nest in which she lays and incubates for 12–14 days a clutch of between three and six white eggs covered with grey-brown streaks and blotches. Both sexes feed the young, which fledge in about a fortnight. It is thought that

Starlings are always the first to make use of free offerings.

as many as three broods may be produced over a period of a month but it is difficult to be sure since sparrows use the nest all through the year and if it is not used for breeding then it serves as a good warm roost – a unique feature of house-sparrow behaviour. No wonder that they are fearless in defence of their little bit of roof space!

Starling *Sturnus vulgaris*

The starling is as common as the house sparrow as a breeding bird, but its population is swollen by winter immigrants, which often gather together in roosts and circle and sweep around before settling for the night. It now seems to have fully recovered from a major decline reported by ornithologists during the eighteenth and early nineteenth centuries. As with many common birds, the sheer beauty of the starling often goes unnoticed since familiarity does breed contempt. Its real splendour is seen just after a heavy shower of April rain has cleaned the feathers, which then reflect the early morning rays of spring sunshine. The plump 21 centimetre (8½ inch) bird shows a green iridescent plumage, the winter feathers of the female being delightfully spangled, which enables the watcher to separate her from the less well endowed male and, at the end of the breeding season, from the even duller juveniles. In flight the triangular wings easily distinguish the starling from birds of the same size.

Like the sparrow, this species often chooses to nest in loose colonies although the odd pair prefers to nest alone. It would seem that the original nest site was a hole in a tree in woodland, but starlings have readily adapted to town life and almost any cavity will be used – even a hole in the ground has been recorded on several occasions. The season commences in April and the male builds an untidy nest before selecting his mate. The nest is then lined by the female. Both birds spend 12–13 days incubating the four to nine pale-blue eggs and the young are also jointly tended and fly in about three weeks. As a general rule starlings have just one brood but the occasional pair finds the time and energy to raise two.

Of all town birds it is the starling which gives the most enjoyment to the folk who share its habitat and this is due entirely to its exceptional powers of mimicry. Apart from copies from the world of nature, trim phones, door bells, cats' miaows, breaking glass and typewriters are all faithfully copied and some scientists wonder why starlings do this. Is it for fun? There seems to be no completely satisfactory answer, but I do wonder if the noises made confuse potential predators. Would a kestrel go near a cat? I think not. Would an owl approach a hole with the sound of a dog growling issuing from it? No! It may well be that mimicry has survival value and is a factor in the undoubted success of the starling.

Kestrel *Falco tinnunculus*

The kestrel, despite the possible defence mechanism of the starling, does not go short of food and is now Britain's most common bird of prey (more than 100,000 breeding pairs), being well represented in towns and along the verges of the motorways connecting cities. It shows marked sexual dimorphism, the male having a rusty-red back covered in small black spots, contrasting with a grey crown, nape, ear coverts, rump and tail, which is long and has a characteristic black terminal band. There is also a narrow but clearly marked moustachial stripe. The underparts are light-brown to yellow, again heavily spotted. The tail of the female is chestnut and so are the upper parts, which are covered with dark bars and the moustachial stripe, although present, is nowhere nearly so marked.

Window-ledges and old churches or warehouses make ideal nesting habitat for the kestrel which uses no nesting material but may make the pretence of scraping a hollow into which the four or five eggs, pale in ground colour but often heavily blotched with rusty brown, are laid. These are incubated for about a month, mainly by the female, but until the young fly at around 30 days both parents bring food. This consists mainly of mammals (there are plenty of rats and mice in towns), insects and some small birds. I watched one nest near Manchester's main street in which the youngsters were fed

The kestrel – our most common bird of prey.

entirely on starlings – despite their mimicry. I once saw a kestrel hover and kill a pied wagtail on a football ground with a First Division match in full swing, and another swoop on a young house sparrow in Horse Guards Parade the day after the trooping of the colour.

Birds of open spaces in towns

Pied wagtail *Motacilla alba*
'Little Trotty Wagtail' was a poem written by John Clare, the peasant naturalist–poet

The kestrel or 'windhover'.

The pied wagtail's tail helps it to balance.

who bemoaned the loss of his native Northamptonshire countryside, but he would probably be amazed to find how well 'Trotty' has adapted to life in busy towns. The pied wagtail is the third member of the wagtail family to occur in Britain, the resident grey occupying a niche in the highland reaches of the rivers, and the summer visiting yellow favouring water meadows. Now we find Clare's pied wagtail having moved from the villages to the busy town but maintaining its own specialised niche unchallenged by other members of its family. The move has been a happy one since the slim, well balanced 18 centimetre (just over 7 inch) bird has a breeding population of about 500,000 pairs. Its food is typically insects but it is a reasonably good scavenger and is often found in school playgrounds where crisps and other unconsidered trifles have been dropped. I have also watched them successfully hunting for earthworms on sports fields where heavy rain may drive them from their flooded burrows. In winter pied wagtails tend to roost in town centres where it is warmer and I had my most embarrassing moment – from an ornithological viewpoint at least – when I attempted to photograph an evening gathering of pied wagtails on the window-ledges of a Lancashire police station. It was only when the heavy hand of the law felt my collar that I realised that I was photographing the cells and the bobby thought I was planning to 'spring' a criminal!

The precise classification of the species has been the subject of some controversy but most workers now accept that the bird which the British call the pied wagtail should be given the scientific name of *Motacilla alba yarellii* to distinguish it from *Motacilla alba alba*, the white wagtail. The latter subspecies is found in all European countries except Britain and Denmark but it does turn up in Britain during periods of hard weather. The young birds of the two races or subspecies cannot be reliably distinguished from each other – a sure sign that they have separated only recently. The adult males, however, show clear distinctions: the British pieds have black backs in the winter whilst the back of the continental whites is grey. In breeding plumage the cock pied wagtail has a lovely black crown, throat and breast whilst the wings are greyish brown. There are neat areas of white on the forehead, cheeks and sides of the neck and on the underbelly. The tail is black but the outer feathers are white and show up clearly in flight. The female is not quite so spruce and has less black on her head and breast. In winter, apart from the black back, the males have a white throat bordered by a crescent-shaped black patch on the breast.

The nest of the pied wagtail is sited in holes in walls, old huts and in towns in derelict and sometimes not so derelict buildings. Generally the nest is built of dried grass lined with fine vegetation and hair or feathers. The clutch size varies from three to seven and the eggs are pale but are often spotted with brown or black. The female incubates these for about a fortnight and both sexes feed the young until they fly in just over a fortnight. Thus there is ample time for the pair to rear two and sometimes three broods.

Black redstart *Phoenicurus ochrurus*
Black redstarts were originally birds of the mountain tops and boulder-strewn screes, but have found untidy heaps of industrial debris an acceptable habitat and the British population and range has been expanding slowly but surely. They were the subject of an in-depth inquiry by the British Trust for Ornithology in 1977, the results of which were summarised by Robert Morgan in the journal *BTO News* of summer 1978:

'The Black Redstart population of Britain has been reported in a series of papers in *British Birds* by Richard Fitter since the 1940s, when the species started to breed regularly in any

numbers. The papers published so far give the number of breeding pairs and territory holding males up to 1973, with data gleaned from an annual search of the county bird reports. The graph gives the published figures from 1940–73 as well as the results of a search of the 1974–76 bird reports. Unfortunately not all of the 1976 reports are yet available and the figure for that year is undoubtedly too low (marked with a star on the graph).

1977 was the first time that observers were asked to actively search the country for Black Redstarts. A total of 60 pairs were proved to breed out of a grand total of 100 territory holding males recorded. This is the first time that the British Black Redstart population has been known to reach three figures, although in the last five years the counts have been consistently higher than ever before. However, it is difficult to be certain how much extra effort was made in 1977 over a "normal" year. There was certainly not a marked increase in the population, which might suggest that the method of going through the bird reports each year gives a sufficiently accurate picture of the situation.

Several areas, including Hampshire, Buckinghamshire, Berkshire and Bedfordshire, had a poor showing in 1977. However, the most noticeable decrease came in Norfolk, where only four territories were reported. This was not the case in Suffolk where 19 territories were found. It is not yet clear whether Norfolk suffered a genuine decrease or suffered from a change in coverage, as this county normally holds 12 or more territories.

From the northern counties of Nottinghamshire, Yorkshire and Lancashire there were 14 records representing a welcome extension of the normal range and numbers, although without observers making special visits to built up and industrial areas, pairs of Black Redstarts could easily go undetected for some time.

As well as recording the presence or absence of Black Redstarts, observers also collected some useful information on breeding. Some 40 clutches or broods were observed, of which nine pairs attempted a second brood.'

The cock birds of both the common and the

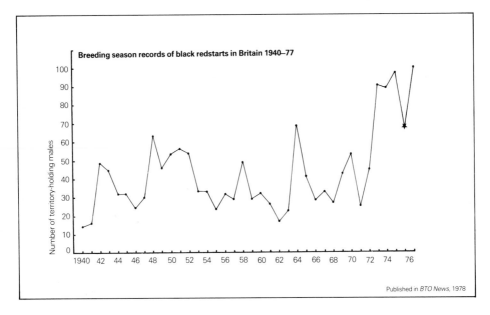

Breeding season records of black redstarts in Britain 1940–77

Published in *BTO News*, 1978

Black redstarts often spend the winter in towns.

black redstart have a red rump and tail from which they derive their name, since *steort* is the old English word for tail. The male black redstart has glossy black plumage with a white patch on the wing. Young males are much duller and often lack the wing patch. Females are a dark brown above with a paler brown below. In winter the males are dark grey-blue and although the wing patch is still present it is much less distinct. The species is often defined as a passage migrant but there does seem to be an increased tendency for the bird to remain throughout the winter. As the food consists mainly of insects, cold weather could prove fatal, but at such times the black redstart feeds along the strand line of beaches. In an article published in the British Naturalists' Association's journal *Country-Side*, Will Bown makes this point very clearly, and it would seem that it is food supply which affects migration. The common redstart has not learned to tap the coastal food supply where the salt prevents freezing and it must therefore migrate. As Will Bown points out:

'Although black redstarts occur in Britain mainly as rather localised summer visitors, and passage migrants from the Continent, a few find some southern counties of England tolerable enough to allow them to stay during the winter.

A number of these cheery little birds, with their smoky plumage and flashing red tails, are thinly scattered along parts of the Dorset coast in winter, quietly picking a living where they can. Some tend to be elusive or easily overlooked along wilder stretches and around small deserted bays. Other individuals are noticed making winter visits to inland sites, to ancient earthworks, military grounds, old quarry workings, occasionally town centres, even a coal yard. At most of these the birds remain distant, but at one favoured spot they allow a close approach, and I have been fortunate to watch a few of them for short spells almost daily through two winters.

A small number are present in a little sheltered cove, where the rough stony shore is backed by a sea-wall and steep, bushy slope. A major attraction for the black redstarts is a relative abundance of the so-called "kelp flies" (*Coelopidae*), which emanate from deep piles of moist tide-wrack along the shore, and which, from observation, certainly seem to form a primary item of diet there.

Over a period of many days flies are to be seen leaving the weed and climbing the sea-wall. The patient redstarts, some less patient pied wagtails, and sometimes other species, position themselves along the wall and simply pick off the flies as they reach the top. Whenever a big tide in the cove causes a large scale emigration from the weed the birds are quickly joined in their feast by starlings, pipits, wrens and various other species, all seen on the wall together. During these mass movements colossal numbers of flies may be involved moving purposefully up and across to the back of the sea-wall in their thousands, to a safe retreat beneath storm-cast stones and debris piled at the foot of the slope (or in the beard and trouser legs of redstart observers).

Throughout the milder days the redstarts and wagtails appear to satisfy their needs with little trouble and seem to spend their time almost casually on the wall. But there are vastly different days, too. In freezing or bad weather, sleet or snow, or when a biting east wind chills the cove, and wild winter seas have played havoc with the food-rich weed along the shore, the flies remain hidden and can be very hard to find, and for the birds it becomes much more an exercise in survival. The redstarts begin to show their superb fly-catching technique. Vertical leaps and aerial loops, short flashing flights along the face of the sea-wall, and sudden swirling dashes around rocks and weed on the shore, effectively startling any sluggish fly into betraying its presence. When alarmed the stupid flies tumble about in circles, but they are easily taken. Massive lumps of weathered limestone, part of the sea defences piled along the shore nearby, often harbour a fly or two on a cold day and the meticulous redstarts are anxious to find every one down amongst this damp and sheltered haven.

When the weather stays stubbornly cold or wild, and flies are difficult to find and the redstarts are having to work hard, it's rather an irony that within inches, almost beneath their feet, is the food they so desire in abundance.

Little ringed plover – the breeding population in Britain is increasing rapidly.

Quantities of flies, clustered together, hidden away beneath the stones and debris. If only then the little black redstart could just turn over a stone or two.

Without ringing the birds it is quite impossible to know whether individuals remain in the cove for any length of time, even all winter, or make only occasional visits in a round of feeding sites. Evidently, though, the cove offers reasonably good feeding conditions most of the time, since black redstarts – even if not the same individuals – are almost always to be found there. The kelp flies are evidently entirely palatable, and the birds themselves, although very few in number, are cheerful enough to brighten even the most miserable of winter days.'

Little ringed plover *Charadrius dubius*

In contrast with the black redstart, the little ringed plover has not solved the problem of finding food in winter and is an out-and-out migrant. However, the breeding population has risen rapidly since the first record in 1938. This was at Tring in Hertfordshire and the total has now passed beyond 500 pairs, assisted by an increase in the number of gravel pits and the closing down of many heavy industries, the sites of which are now derelict. Apart from the difference in habitat, the little ringed plovers can be distinguished by the absence of a wing bar, which can be clearly seen in the flying common ringed plover. Indeed, the little ringed is the only plover which lacks a wing bar and its 'pee-oo' call is also diagnostic. The legs of the ringed plover are orange-yellow whilst those of the little ringed plover are pink and the latter species also has a very prominent yellow ring round the eye. The ringed plover has a reddish-yellow bill with a black tip whilst that of the little ringed is mainly black with only a small patch of reddish-yellow near the base.

Once a coastal nester like the ringed plover, the little ringed has since 1940 moved inland and now favours such sites as disused (and occasionally functioning) railway embankments, old steelworks and coal yards, and also the edges of gravel pits. Within the confines of a disused brickworks less than 8 kilometres (5 miles) from the centre of Manchester I watched a pair incubating their clutch of four pointed yellow-brown dark-spotted eggs. This took them 25 days and by mid-June the young were scuttling around, and after some three weeks they had taken their maiden flight. There seems every reason to suppose that the population of this attractive 15 centimetre (6 inch) wader will continue to increase but one thing could hinder this – landscaping. Invariably this means that the old industrial sites are ploughed up and grassed over. What seems to be public-spirited is often disastrous to wildlife, and naturalists would be much happier if part of, but not all, the habitat was landscaped, with areas left for such birds as the black redstart and little ringed plover. In other words, let nature do her own landscaping. Trees should be planted for cover, and this should also be the aim of those who plan town and city parks.

Birds of parkland

One of the great attributes of the leisure and recreation departments is that they produce attractive human habitats with lovely flowers, neat lines of trees, and splashing fountains. Their drawback, from the naturalist's point of view, is that they abhor rosebay willow herb, nettles and brambles and root them out or spray them unmercifully with herbicides.

Hollow trees are 'unsightly' and are felled, the trunk being carted away and not left to go rotten and offend the critical eye of the well groomed visitor. What is urgently required is a 'wild area' set aside where 'weeds' are allowed to grow, hollow grub-full trees are left to rot in peace and birds can move in and find ample food. These will then delight the visitor and maybe gather in the picnic sites to beg the odd crumb. The same rules could well be applied to house gardens, where a wild corner can often treble the number of bird species feeding and breeding in the area. Birds found regularly in park and garden are the wren, the song thrush and the mistle thrush, while rarities such as the waxwing can often be persuaded to remain if shrubs such as cotoneaster are planted, whose berries provide food during the hard cold winter. An increasingly common and therefore decreasingly popular visitor to parks and gardens is the intelligent scavenging and often predatory magpie.

Wren *Troglodytes troglodytes*
The wren is arguably Britain's most numerous breeding species and as many as 10 million pairs may be an accurate estimate, although severe winters do have a devastating effect upon this figure. The tiny 9·6 centimetre (just under 4 inches) bird finds most of its food on the ground amongst the dead leaves and it is just this habitat which is affected by hard frost, and the apparent reluctance of the wren to accept offerings on bird tables accounts for population plunges, though its reproductive efficiency ensures a quick recovery. The song is a quickly linked warble, clear and shrill and, for a small bird, loud and wildly exciting, uttered from a low perch or even in flight. The male has courtship on his mind from as early as February to as late as August, but he has a lot of work to do before being accepted by a female. He often builds as many as a dozen domed nests (from which the scientific name, which means 'cave dweller', derives), but he does not line any of them. Instead he takes the female on a tour of inspection and it is she who adds the final cosy feather lining to the structure of moss, dried grass and leaves. The hen then assumes

Wren – a tough little bird which suffers badly in
hard winters.

dominance by incubating the clutch of from three to eleven pale red-spotted eggs for 14 days, after which the male helps to feed the young. They fledge after about 17 days, thus giving ample time for a second clutch to be raised.

Wrens are another species which are more often heard than seen, and most visual contacts involve a whirr of wings and a rustly little dot buzzing from one clump of dense vegetation to another. Then, after a moment's silence, a stream of alarm notes belies the size of the plump little bird with its short cocked-up tail. There are fewer more pugnacious characters in the bird world than the wren, but parks and gardens do have more than their fair share of accomplished songsters and the dawn chorus can entrance those of us who wake up in suburbia on a fine May morning. Prominent amongst these songsters is always the aptly named song thrush.

Song thrush *Turdus philomelos*

With its breeding population of about 3½ million pairs the song thrush is not so common as the blackbird which is possibly twice as common. However, the song thrush is much more common than the mistle thrush (*Turdus viscivorus*), of which there are about half a million pairs. The 22·5 centimetre (9 inch) song thrush can be distinguished from the 26 centimetre (10½ inch) mistle thrush by its yellowish breast with large dark spots. The breast of the mistle thrush is paler and the spots are larger, rounder and more distinct whilst the outer tail feathers are outlined in white, which shows clearly in flight. Some song thrushes do move south in autumn, but most are resident and are joined in winter by the slightly smaller 22 centimetre (8¾ inch) redwing (*Turdus musicus*), which has red

Song thrush feeding its young.

Mistle thrush at its nest on a school window-sill.

under its wing as its name indicates; an equally obvious distinction is the prominent eyestrip which is totally lacking in the song thrush. Apart from the ring ouzel already described, the thrush family regularly present in Britain is completed by the fieldfare (*Turdus pilaris*), which often accompanies redwings on feeding forays to field and parkland. The fieldfare is 25 centimetres (10 inches) in length and can be recognised by its blue-grey head, dark russet back, grey rump and black tail. The breast is reddish-yellow liberally striped with black, and the bird is streaked with the same colour on its flanks. In recent years, possibly due to the average British summer being cooler and damper than formerly, both the fieldfare and redwing have bred in Britain, but in very small and variable numbers and mainly in Scotland.

It is the song thrush nest, however, which is usually the first to stir a feeling for nature in young naturalists. The hen builds a wonderfully neat nest of grass or moss solidified with earth and 'cemented' smoothly on the inside by a mixture of mud or perhaps cow or horse dung. Even a single leafy tree in a town garden can serve its purpose and here the hen incubates her clutch of four or five lovely sky-blue eggs marked with black spots for about a fortnight. At the time of hatching the male takes more interest in the proceedings and helps to feed the young until they fly on or about their fourteenth day. Two clutches and sometimes three are raised by the end of the season, which can go on into September during a reasonable summer. The main diet of the song thrush is insects but in the winter it can turn to berries and household scraps. It does, however, have one unique piece of feeding behaviour in the way it deals with molluscs with hard shells such as snails. These are carried to a stone against which they are continually battered until they are broken and the thrush gets at the nutritious flesh within. Each bird seems to have a favourite stone

Redwing (**top**) and fieldfare (**bottom**).
Both winter visitors to Britain.

which becomes surrounded by a litter of broken shells. These are called thrushes' anvils.

I have noticed in recent years that blackbirds, which have not yet learned to copy the act, wait for the thrush to break the snail shell and then dart in and pinch the morsel. Blackbirds invariably prove able to dominate most other species at the bird table and a sort of pecking order can be worked out when watching birds from one's own lounge window.

I am often asked how to prevent birds flying into the window when the bird table is close by and why birds attack their own re-flections. Obviously birds attack their own reflection because they think it is a rival. There is a simple cure. Place a cardboard cut-out the shape of a bird of prey close to the window and put the bird table to the side of the window so that birds on the table cannot see the 'hawk' but so that it comes into sight if they perch on the window-ledge or fly close to it. Feeding birds in winter, especially in cold spells, can often bring the reward of a real rarity, especially if you plant cotoneaster in the garden as the red berries are an unfailing attraction to the waxwing, a most spectacular if irregular winter visitor.

Waxwing *Bombycilla garrulus*

The waxwing is an 18 centimetre (7 inch) rufous-coloured species with a drooping crest,

A thrush's 'anvil'. Here a thrush has brought large numbers of snails and has broken open the shells by hammering them on the stone so that it can eat the soft bodies inside.

lovely rich chestnut on the under-tail coverts, and a wide yellow band across the black tail. The rump is grey and the wings brown with yellow and white markings and with red waxy spots on the secondary feathers, from which the species gets its common name. It belongs to a small family, the *bombycillidae*, which is concentrated in the coniferous and birch forests of Scandinavia. In winter the population, which feeds on berries such as rowan, moves south into central Europe, but if the berry crop fails or if the population is inflated by a fruitful breeding season then the population 'explodes' and waxwing years occur in unusual places such as Britain. Such invasions are never predictable but there does seem to be an approximate ten-year cycle. It has been suggested that a glut of food one year may mean that more birds survive the harsh winter and the following year the normal berry crop is unable to support the popula-

tion. The reason is, however, not absolutely certain whereas in the case of the magpie we can be sure of our facts and state with certainty that of all the many species described in this book this one has benefited most from human activities. It is therefore fitting that the magpie should be the last bird to be described.

Magpie *Pica pica*

The magpie has a white belly and two white shoulder patches. The rest of the plumage is black, but in reflected sunlight a bluish iridescence is attractive, as is the green and bronze sheen on the tail feathers. The length is about 45 centimetres (18 inches) but about half of this is taken up by the tail and the slender body weighs only 210 grams (7½ oz). There seems to have been quite a dramatic decrease during the nineteenth century, doubtless due to the attentions of game-keepers and the like. Apart from in East Anglia, where agricultural chemicals may have had an effect on the magpie population, the species has increased dramatically since the 1950s, a trend which still continues with a breeding population now exceeding 250,000 pairs. Like others of the crow family magpies are omnivorous feeders which have readily accepted human 'throw-away' foods found on refuse dumps and in dustbins outside town restaurants. We have also assisted the bird in its comeback in the countryside by slaughtering its natural enemies, the goshawk and the peregrine.

The nests are constructed in trees or the tall hedges of gardens and parks, magpies being especially fond of hawthorn, which gives protection to the twiggy domed nest lined with mud and thin hair. Only the female incubates the clutch of four to eight light-green eggs which are liberally spotted with grey and brown. She begins to incubate before the clutch is complete and each egg hatches between the 18th and the 20th day following laying. Both parents feed the young, which fly when they are between the 22nd and the 27th day following hatching. Large populations of magpies are something of a menace since they are not averse to raiding the nests of other species. The question therefore arises should magpies and other potentially predatory species be culled in bird reserves where rare species are struggling to breed successfully?

In some cases culling common birds such as gulls and magpies is necessary if other species are to survive – but culling does not allow nature to balance her own books, is a short term, not a long term answer and is no answer at all when the threat to wildlife lies beyond the confines of a reserve. The custodians of a bird reserve, say, on the Cumbrian coast close to Sellafield can scarcely relax simply because their reserve has a notice saying 'Keep out, birds breeding' over the gate. Similarly, a beach habitat may have the full protection of the law, but what happens when an oil slick is driven in by the wind? What happens to a lake, or a stretch of river, or a delicately balanced moor with a woodland fringe, when acid rain – perhaps produced in another country hundreds of miles away – pours down on the habitat? What happens when agricultural chemicals are flushed down a river, enter the ocean currents and affect the breeding of birds thousands of miles from the source of the pollutant? While one country blames another, birds and other forms of wildlife die.

Obviously, there is no room for chauvinistic isolation on the part of ornithologists. Neither is there any sense in undocumented accusations against industries or governments indiscriminately charging them with neglecting the environment. Both discussion and cooperation are badly needed both at the national and the international level – and before the effect of a pollutant can be measured a bird population must be counted regularly. Yet, no government can afford a perpetual census, so this is one important way in which the amateur naturalist can help the professional, since regular bird censuses can indicate the improving state of the environment – or the converse, as in the case of the shag population mentioned in Chapter 4.

When facts and figures like these are needed, naturalists' diaries and regular field trips organised by naturalists' groups to monitor their local environment can be of enormous value. A member of one such group once asked me if the records of their field trips were useful in the context of Britain's wildlife. I replied that I hoped not, by which I meant that I would of course be happiest if the environment in that area remained healthy. But what if it did not remain healthy? How would we know that a bird population was being adversely affected, if we were unaware of its past population and had nothing to compare it with? And how, unless we know a particular habitat and its environment intimately, can we monitor its health and stand a chance of improving its condition? That is why it is so vital to understand just how each species fits into its habitat and exactly how it relates to the natural and human world around it.

Useful addresses

ASSOCIATION OF SCHOOL NATURAL HISTORY SOCIETIES c/o Strand School, Elm Park. London SW2.

BRITISH BIRDS MAGAZINE Fountains, Blunham, Bedford MK44 3NJ.

BRITISH BROADCASTING CORPORATION NATURAL HISTORY UNIT Whiteladies Road, Bristol BS8 2LR.

BRITISH NATURALISTS' ASSOCIATION Thorneyholme Hall, Roughlee, near Burnley BB12 9LH.

BRITISH ORNITHOLOGISTS UNION c/o Zoological Society of London, Regent's Park, London NW1 4RY.

BRITISH TRUST FOR ORNITHOLOGY Beech Grove, Tring, Hertfordshire HP23 5NR.

COUNTRYSIDE COMMISSION 1 Cambridge Gate, Regent's Park, London NW1 4JY.

FIELD STUDIES COUNCIL 9 Devereux Court, Strand, London WC2R 3JR.

FORESTRY COMMISSION 25 Savile Row, London W1X 2AY.

GAME CONSERVANCY COUNCIL Fordingbridge, Hampshire.

INTERNATIONAL COUNCIL FOR BIRD PRESERVATION 219c Huntington Road, Cambridge CB3 0DL.

MAMMAL SOCIETY Harvest House, Reading, Berkshire.

MEN OF THE TREES Crawley Down, Crawley, Sussex.

NATIONAL FARMERS UNION Agriculture House, Knightsbridge, London SW1.

NATIONAL TRUST 42 Queen Anne's Gate, London SW1.

NATURE CONSERVANCY 19 Belgrave Square, London SW1.

NORTHERN IRELAND ORNITHOLOGISTS CLUB 20 Ardvarna Crescent, Belfast BT4 2GJ.

ROYAL SOCIETY FOR NATURE CONSERVATION The Green, Nettleham, Lincolnshire LN2 2NR.

ROYAL SOCIETY FOR THE PROTECTION OF BIRDS The Lodge, Sandy, Bedfordshire SG19 2DL.

SEABIRD GROUP Department of Zoology, Aberdeen University, Tillydrone Avenue, Aberdeen AB9 2TN.

SCOTTISH ORNITHOLOGISTS CLUB 21 Regent Terrace, Edinburgh EH7 5BT.

SCOTTISH WILDLIFE TRUST 8 Dublin Street, Edinburgh EH1 3PP.

SOCIETY FOR THE PROMOTION OF NATURE RESERVES The Manor House, Alford, Lincolnshire.

WILDFOWL TRUST Slimbridge, Gloucestershire GL2 7BT

WOODLAND TRUST Westgate, Grantham, Lincolnshire NG31 6LL.

WORLD PHEASANT ASSOCIATION Daws Hall, Lamarsh, Bures, Suffolk CO8 5EX.

WORLD WILDLIFE FUND Panda House, 11–13 Ockford Road, Godalming, Surrey GU7 1QU.

Bibliography

ALEXANDER, W. B.   *Birds of the Ocean* (Pitman, 1955).

ARDLEY, N.   *Birds of Towns* (Almark, 1975).

AUSTIN, O. L., and SINGER, A.   *Birds of the World* (Hamlyn, 1961).

BARNES, J. A. G.   *The Titmice of the British Isles* (David & Charles, 1975).

BOAG, D.   *The Kingfisher* (Blandford, 1982).

BROWN, L.   *British Birds of Prey* (Collins, 1976).

BROWN, L.   *Birds of Prey, Their Biology and Ecology* (Hamlyn, 1976).

BUNN, D. S., WARBURTON, A. B., and WILSON, R. D. S.   *The Barn Owl* (Poyser, 1982).

CAMPBELL, B.   *The Crested Tit,* Forestry Commission Record No. 98 (1974).

CAMPBELL, B., and FERGUSON-LEES, L. J.   *A Field Guide to Birds' Nests* (Constable, 1972).

COOMBS, C. J. F.   *The Crows* (Batsford, 1978).

CRAMP, S., and SIMMONS, K. E. L.   *Handbook of the Birds of Europe, the Middle East and North Africa,* Vols I and II (continuing), (Oxford University Press, 1977, 1980).

DARLINGTON, A.   *Natural History Atlas of Great Britain* (Warne, 1969).

DURMAN, R. (ed.)   *Bird Observatories in Britain and Ireland* (Poyser, 1976).

EASTMAN, R.   *The Kingfisher* (Collins, 1969).

ELKINS, N.   *Weather and Bird Behaviour* (Poyser, 1983).

EVERETT, M.   *The Natural History of Owls* (Hamlyn, 1977).

EVERETT, M.   *The Golden Eagle* (Blackwood, 1977).

FISHER, J.   *The Fulmar* (Collins, 1952).

FISHER, J., and FLEGG, J.   *Watching Birds* (Poyser, 1974).

FISHER, J., and LOCKLEY, R. M.   *Seabirds* (Collins, 1954).

FLEGG, JIM   *In Search of Birds* (Blandford, 1983).

FREETHY, RON   *The Making of the British Countryside* (David & Charles, 1981).

FREETHY, RON   *How Birds Work* (Blandford, 1982).

FREETHY, RON   *The Naturalists' Guide to the British Coastline* (David & Charles, 1983).

FULLER, R. J.   *Bird Habitats in Britain* (Poyser, 1982).

GOODERS, J.   *Where to Watch Birds in Britain and Europe* (André Deutsch, 1970).

HALE, W. G.   *Waders* (Collins, 1980).

HOWARD, E.   *A Waterhen's World* (Cambridge University Press, 1940).

HUDSON, W. H.   *Birds in London* (Longmans Green, 1898).

LACK, D.   *Swifts in a Tower* (Chapman & Hall, 1973).

LOCKLEY, R. M.   *Shearwaters* (Collins, 1942).

LOVE, JOHN   *The Return of the Sea Eagle* (Cambridge University Press, 1983).

MURTON, R. K.   *Man and Birds* (Collins, 1971).

NELSON, B.   *The Gannet* (Poyser, 1978).

NELSON, B.   *Seabirds, Their Biology and Ecology* (Hamlyn, 1980).

NEWTON, I.   *Finches* (Collins, 1972).

NEWTON, I.   *Population Ecology of Raptors* (Poyser, 1979).

OGILVIE, M. A.   *Wild Ducks of Britain and Europe* (Poyser, 1975).

OGILVIE, M. A.   *Wild Geese* (Poyser, 1978).

OGILVIE, M. A.   *The Bird Watcher's Guide to the Wetlands of Britain* (Batsford, 1979).

ORTON, D. A.   *The Merlins of the Welsh Marshes* (David & Charles, 1980).

PALMAR, C. E.   *Woodpeckers in Woodlands,* Forestry Commission Record No. 92 (1974).

PALMAR, C. E.   *The Capercaillie,* Forestry Commission Forest Record No. 109 (1976).

PARSLOW, J. L. F.   *Breeding Birds in Britain and Ireland* (Poyser, 1973).

PERRINS, C. M.   *British Tits* (Collins, 1978).

PERRY, R.   *Watching Sea Birds* (Croom Helm, 1975).

PETERSON, R. T., MOUNTFORD, G., and HOLLOM, P. A. D.   *A Field Guide to Birds of Britain and Europe* (Collins, 1974, 1983).

PRATER, A. J.   *Estuary Birds in Britain and Ireland* (Poyser, 1973).

PRESTT, IAN   *British Birds' Lifestyles and Habitats* (Batsford, 1982).

RATCLIFFE, D.   *The Peregrine Falcon* (Poyser, 1980).

SHARROCK, J. T. R. (ed.)   *The Atlas of Breeding Birds in Britain and Ireland* (Poyser, 1976).

SIMMS, E.   *Woodland Birds* (Collins, 1971).

SIMMS, E.   *Birds of Town and Suburb* (Collins, 1975).

SIMMS, E.   *British Thrushes* (Collins, 1978).

SIMMS, E.   *The Public Life of the Street Pigeon* (Hutchinson, 1979).

SPARKS, J., and SOPER, A.   *Owls, Their History and Natural History* (David & Charles, 1970).

SUMMERS-SMITH, J. D.   *The House Sparrow* (Collins, 1963).

TINBERGEN, N.   *The Herring Gull's World* (Collins, 1953).

TUCK, G., and HEINZEL, H.   *A Field Guide to the Seabirds of Britain and the World* (Collins, 1978).

VAUGHAN, R.   *Plovers* (Terence Dalton, 1980).

VESEY-FITZGERALD, B.   *British Game* (Collins, 1946).

WATSON, D.   *The Hen Harrier* (Poyser, 1977).

WILMORE, S. B.   *Crows, Jays and Ravens* (David & Charles, 1975).

WITHERBY, JOURDAIN, TICEHURST and TUCKER   *Handbook of British Birds* (5 vols) (Witherby, 1939–46).

WYLLIE, I.   *The Cuckoo* (Batsford, 1981).

YALDEN, D. W.   *The Identification of the Remains in Owl Pellets* (Mammal Society, 1977).

YAPP, W. B.   *Birds and Woods* (Oxford University Press, 1962).

YAPP, W. B.   *The Life and Organisation of Birds* (Arnold, 1970).

Index

Bold numerals denote numbers of black and white photographs. Italic numerals denote page numbers of line drawings. Plate numbers refer to colour photographs.

Latin names of species are given in the subheadings or in the text and have not been included in the index.